THE EVERLASTING
HATRED
THE ROOTS OF JIHAD

ACKNOWLEDGEMENTS

I would like to thank my friend, Joe Farah, CEO of the internationally acclaimed news website, **www.worldnetdaily.com**, for his indispensable help in researching this book. He is a brilliant reporter and writer and he helped me in many ways during the course of this work.

I would also like to give a special thanks to author, historian and reporter, Joan Peters. Her best-selling book, *From Time Immemorial*, has been my constant companion and reference source for over fifteen years. This is the most accurate, best researched and documented work I have found on the secular issues of modern Israeli-Arab conflict. I strongly recommend this book. It can be purchased through: **www.worldnetdaily.com**

HAL LINDSEY

THE EVERLASTING HATRED
THE ROOTS OF JIHAD

ORACLE HOUSE™
PUBLISHING

Everlasting Hatred

Oracle House Publishing, Murrieta 92562

Cover design: Daniel Cox.

Cover photos: AP/Wide World Photos.

ISBN 1-931628-15-7

Library of Congress Control Number: 2002108185

Printed in the United States of America.

Printed by UBS Printing Group, Inc. Corona, CA

CONTENTS

Falsehoods Discovered • Overlooking The Obvious • Underlings Secretly
Reverse Foreign Policy Of Their Nation • Britain Enacts Harsher
Restrictions on Jews • The Infamous White Paper • The Passfield-White
Paper • Israel 'Downsized' Again • Accessories to Mass Murder • The
Turning Point • The Price of Britain's Betrayal

CHAPTER ONE

We're At War: Islam's 'Jihad' Against the West

"Over the rest of this decade, the divide between radical Islam and the industrial democracies will become the most destabilizing factor in world affairs."

JOSEPH DE COURCY, INTELLIGENCE DIGEST, JANUARY 24, 1992

"Although its [terrorist organizations'] separate parts may have local objectives and take part in local conflicts, the main motivation driving the terror network is an anti-western hostility that seeks to achieve nothing less than a reversal of history. It seeks to roll back the West and install an extremist form of Islam as the dominant power in the world . . .

What is at stake today in nothing less than the survival of our civilization."

BENJAMIN NETANYAHU, FORMER PRIME MINISTER OF ISRAEL

"The governments of the world should know that Islam cannot be defeated. Islam will be victorious in all the countries of the world, and Islam and the teachings of the Koran will prevail all over the world."

AYATOLLAH RUHOLLAH KHOMEINI OF IRAN

The video shows the tortured face of an American news reporter named Daniel Pearl. He is forced to confess, "My father is a Jew, my mother is a Jew and I am a Jew." Then suddenly a hand with a knife appears on the video screen and slashes his throat. Then his head is hacked off and held aloft by a hand in front of the camera. The video cuts to his murderers repeatedly stabbing his lifeless corpse. The final scene cuts to Pearl's head lying on a pile of newspapers as a message scrolls across the screen: "If our demands are not met, there will be more like this."

These Islamic terrorists chose Daniel Pearl to slaughter for one reason—he is a Jew. But the fact that he was an American cannot be overlooked. The gory details of Pearl's videotaped murder are evidence of the maniacal hatred of the movement to which they belong, Islamic Fundamentalism. But it is only one of thousands of crimes committed by these religious fanatics in history—and all for the same cause; they hate Jews with a visceral, bone-deep hatred that is almost impossible for the Western civilization to comprehend. In fact, this hatred goes back to the dawn of history.

On September 11, 2001, Americans were suddenly thrust into the middle of this same hatred. It is part of an ancient family feud. We were actually involved in this conflict long before we realized either its magnitude or its ultimate destiny. But after September 11, Americans are frantically groping to understand it. Many questions continue to be asked after the shock of those initial days and their aftermath.

Some Imperative Questions

In the light of recent events, most of the Judeo-Christian based Western civilization is asking:

- Why do most Muslims hate Jews?

- Did this hatred begin, as Muslims claim, with the Zionist Movement and the creation of the State of Israel, or is their evidence of this hatred prior to that?

- Why does Muslim Fundamentalism hate the United States and call it "the great Satan?"

- Why would Muslim terrorists willingly sacrifice their own lives to kill Americans?

- Do they hate America only because of our support of Israel, or is their evidence of other reasons?

- Do the Islamic Fundamentalists have access to weapons of mass destruction? If so, will they use them on the United States?

- Could their terrorist organizations imperil the very survival of the United States?

It is the purpose of this book to answer these questions with evidence from history.

In addition, there are even more foundational questions this book will seek to answer, such as:

- Are there calls for violence and conquest in the Koran and in the equally authoritative traditions recorded in the Hadith?

- What does the Koran teach about Judaism and Christianity?

- Are the Islamic Fundamentalists an aberration of the Muslim religion, or are they—as they claim—the true followers of Mohammad?

- Does the example of Mohammad's life teach us the true meaning of the Koran?

- What can we learn from the history of Muslim conquests?

- Were these conquests due to misinterpretations of the Koran or were they commanded by it?

- Can we get insights into Mohammad from his forefathers, Ishmael and Kedar?

- The Muslim religion is tightly interwoven with the culture of the 7th century Arabian Peninsula. Are there things about that culture that will shed light on Muslim beliefs and behavior?

The New Peril We Face

More than at any time since the Crusades, Islam is posing a serious threat to the Western world. It now possesses the wealth and the weaponry to supplant the Soviet Union as the greatest challenge to the United States, Israel and the Western Judeo-Christian based world order.

As the chapter title declares, "We are at war." I wrote back in 1991 that with the fall of the Soviet Union, the greatest danger facing the world was no longer Communism, but Islamic Fundamentalism. But I must say that even I didn't realize how great a threat Islam would become.

How Nice the Old Enemy Looks Now

During the Cold War, we faced an enemy that was somewhat conventional. The Soviets were at work through operatives spreading the gospel of Communism around the world. We fought their surrogates in Korea, Vietnam and South America. They possessed nuclear weapons and had several means of delivering them on target. They also had weapons of mass destruction (WMD), such as biological and chemical weapons, that could kill most of the world's population.

But during this 50-year era, there were certain rational constants to deal with.

If the United States were to be struck by any of the WMDs possessed by the Soviet Union or one of its surrogates, we knew where and how to retaliate. They knew that to attack us meant an instant end to their civilization as well.

In short, as terrible as it was, the tenuous world stability was kept by the doctrine of MAD—Mutually Assured Destruction.

Meet the New Enemy

With the new threat, however, there are entirely new dimensions with enormously greater dangers. We no longer face a political force but a religion that has 1.3 billion followers worldwide.

Islam is the fastest growing religion in the world. And the increasingly radical fundamentalist brand represents not only the greatest threat to world peace and stability, but also the greatest challenge to the Judeo-Christian based western civilization.

To appreciate the growing power and influence of Islam, you must look beyond the population figures. Muslims now control, to some extent, about 50 of the world's most important countries—from Indonesia in the East, through the oil rich states of the Middle East, to Senegal on the Atlantic. These countries control vast wealth and unappreciated commercial resources.

At least 70 of the world's 184 countries are considered part of the Dar al Islam, or house of Islam—land over which Islam rules. It is a religion practiced in the jungles of Africa, the sands of the Sahara, the oil fields of the Middle East, the mountains of Asia and the islands of the Pacific. Islam is also making its impact felt in traditionally Christian parts of the world.

Mosques Replacing Churches in West

Today, in "Bonny Old England", there are more Muslims than Methodists. There are even more Muslims than there are evangelical Christians, and more active Mosques than Churches.[1]

"Funded by the vast resources of Arab oil money, the Muslims are buying abandoned Anglican Churches and turning them into mosques at such a rate that some Muslims claim that England will soon be the first Muslim European country," writes author Robert Morey. About 10 years ago there were an estimated 150 mosques

---

1. Robert Morey, *The Islamic Invasion*, (Eugene, OR: Harvest Publishers, 1992), p. 55–56.

in England. Today there are more than 1,100.[2]

Islam is also growing rapidly in Australia, Canada, Germany and the United States. There are now more than 700 Islamic centers in the US and more Muslims than Episcopalians or Presbyterians. Islam is now numerically on par with Judaism as America's largest minority religion.

Fundamentalism, the Real Threat

At least 10 percent of the 1.3 billion Muslims are Fundamentalists, thus potential terrorist threats. And intelligence information indicates their percentage is growing. History shows that the devout Muslim Fundamentalists are one of the most lethal threats the world has ever known.

In contrast to the old enemy, the new one is powerfully motivated to become a "martyr" or a suicide attacker in the cause of Allah. He is promised the highest and most glorious place in Paradise, with 72 virgins to meet his every desire. Not even the Japanese Kamikaze pilots of World War II can match with the danger these Islamic zealots pose. And the chilling news is that the Fundamentalists are on the brink of possessing the most destructive weapons the world has ever known, thanks to certain terrorist-sponsoring Muslim countries.

Contrary to the old Cold War, we can be hit by a major attack and not know exactly where to retaliate. This enemy hides in the shadows and mingles with citizens within our own nation. He has Muslim sympathizers everywhere who give him aid and shelter. He is also effectively protected by America's doctrine of "political correctness", which has hamstrung our intelligence agencies and rendered him virtually "uncatchable."

As the Islamic world developed untold wealth through oil, its military might has been brought to incredibly lethal strength. The

---

2. Ibid., p. 5.

only thing standing in the way of the Muslim nations achieving some degree of parity with the West is their tendency to fight among themselves. But as you will see, there is one cause that can rally them together—hatred of the Jewish state and anyone who supports it. And Islamic Fundamentalism is the driving force that is rallying all Muslims to "Jihad" to destroy Israel and replace the Western world order.

Is the United States in Mortal Danger?

Since September 11, many Americans are wondering just how vulnerable are we. Is our nation truly in grave danger?

Here is just a sampling of warnings given by responsible U.S. leaders:

> "The prospect of another attack against the United States is just as real . . . as it was on September 12. It's not a matter of IF, but of WHEN." (Emphasis mine)
>
> VICE PRESIDENT DICK CHENEY, MAY 19, 2002[3]

> "There will be another terrorist attack. We will not be able to stop it . . . I think we will see [walk-in suicide bombers] in the future. I think it's inevitable."
>
> FBI DIRECTOR ROBERT MUELLER, MAY 20, 2002[4]

> "Terrorist networks have relations with terrorist states that have weapons of mass destruction . . . and they will get their hands on them."
>
> SECRETARY OF DEFENSE DONALD RUMSFELD, MAY 21, 2002[5]

In addition, the United States has had the following credible high alerts declared against the following possible terrorist strikes:

- Danger of a strike on our major bridges, such as the Golden Gate or Oakland Bay Bridge

---

3. NEWSWEEK, June 3, 2002, p. 22.

4. Ibid., pp. 22–23.

5. Ibid., p. 23.

- Danger of attack on tunnels entering New York City

- Danger of attack on subways

- Danger of attack on our railways

- Danger of attack in large shopping malls

- Danger of another aircraft hijacking and suicide attack on a major building

- Danger of a strike against the Statue of Liberty

- Danger of a cyber attack on main business networks

- Danger of attack on banks and financial institutions such as stock exchanges

Are Counter Measures Possible?

These warnings came despite the formation of a new Department of Home Security, the complete re-organization of the FBI, maximum alert of the CIA, and US troops in Afghanistan seeking to destroy the operational headquarters of the latest star of the Islamic pantheon of terror organizations—Al-Qaida.

Our country has mobilized for a global war on terrorism, and already it is faltering. The main terrorist states—Iran, Iraq and Syria—have WMDs but appear to be out of our reach. We can't get allies to join us in an attack on them. In fact some of our "allies" continue to sell them components that can be used in WMDs.

The US has had to admit that our own military forces do not presently have the capability to take on any one of these Muslim powers. We can thank the mythological "peace dividend" of the Clinton era for that. All branches of our military were downsized, critical bases were closed, highly trained personnel were lost, weapons were cannibalized and new ones were not acquired. Smart weapons can only do so much; they can't subdue a dangerous country. This is why we haven't seen the last of the Al-Qaida.

Who Is the Terrorist 'Du Jour'?

Even keeping straight who the real terrorists are is almost impossible. President Bush is in an precarious position. He valiantly declared our goal, defined what a terrorist is, both individual and state, and then proceeded to embrace as friends nations that are clearly terrorists by his own definition. This is being done because of obvious economic and political reasons.

In addition to all of these problems:

- Our borders are still as porous as Swiss cheese

- Airport security is still a joke primarily because of the fear of being "politically incorrect." There is no way to correct this apart from firing many people that are not suited for the job and using "racial profiling." The world's best airport security is Israel's. They use aggressive racial profiling and hire their brightest and best to man security. Machines will not take the place of these measures. Minimum wage paid, poorly educated people cannot "psych out" a trained terrorist.

- Our Nuclear Plants are still vulnerable to terrorist attacks because there is no effective "no fly zone" around them. According to military intelligence, a suicide plane can still hit them, and terrorists using SCUBA gear can infiltrate them from adjacent waterways and launch an attack

- Our drinking water and food chain are vulnerable to biological/ chemical attacks.

Face It; We Are in Deep Pooh-Pooh!

I reported the following on a recent *International Intelligence Briefing* broadcast over Trinity Broadcasting Network,

> The possibility of a global holocaust increases on a daily basis.
>
> If it isn't the Islamic/Hindu conflict in South Asia, it's the Islamic jihad against America and the American declara-

tion of war against Islamic terror.

If global war doesn't break out as a consequence of the coming US attacks on Islamic terrorist states like Iraq, Iran, or Syria, it might break out over the Islamic jihad against Israel.

America and Israel have little in common with India—apart from a representative democratic political system—and virtually nothing in common spiritually, but all share a common enemy: Islam.

At this moment in history, Islam represents the single greatest threat to the continued survival of the planet the world has ever seen.

The Relevance of Ancient Issues

I believe all these clear and present dangers can only be understood by learning how this conflict began between the descendants of the Biblical patriarch Abraham four thousand years ago. There is a perfect word that describes the Arab's virulent feelings toward Israel. It is the word "enmity". The dictionary defines enmity as, "the extreme ill will or hatred that exists toward an enemy." It infers a state of hatred that has been nurtured over a long period of time.

At the beginning of the 21st century, it is hard to imagine how a 4000-year-old family feud could cause the whole world to become involved. Yet this is exactly what the Bible predicted would happen in the last days. These prophecies spell out an exact scenario of events that will come together shortly before the end of history as we know it.

Central to this scenario is the re-igniting of the ancient conflict between the Israelites and Arabs. The conflict has risen and subsided at various times since the destruction and dispersion of Israel in 70 AD.

It is as a consequence of the rebirth of the State of Israel that the Bible prophets predict the whole world will become involved.

The Bible specifically predicts what will be the final flashpoint that ignites the war of Armageddon. It will be an unsolvable dispute over Jerusalem between the sons of Isaac and Jacob and the sons of Ishmael and Esau. We know these people today as the Israelis and the Arabs.

Who Would Have Dreamed . . . ?

Who would have believed as the 20th century dawned that a small, backward, neglected land that had become as desolate as the moon would become the center of a controversy so great that all the major world powers would be dragged into it? For centuries, world attention focused on the Gentile civilizations of Europe, the Americas, Russia and the Far East. Until the middle of the 20th century, many people couldn't even find Palestine on a map. But today, the headlines aren't about western or Asian civilizations; they are about the peoples of the Middle East. For the first time in modern history, ancient Biblical names are making global headlines.

One of the main, predicted signs that the world was entering the "last days and the end of history as we know it" was that the strategic center of the world would shift back to the region where history began. Today, the world's focus has returned to a place that had been bypassed by the modern developments of science and technology.

Prepare To Be Shocked

This book will reveal many vital facts about the Middle East conflict that are little known. It will take you into history and reveal the real causes of the growing world crisis. Writing this book has been a great sobering adventure. So press on through the history and facts, I promise it will be rewarding. And I believe you will find a vital basis for hope in the coming perilous times.

CHAPTER TWO

How It All Began

Emperor Napoleon Bonaparte, while on his Palestinian campaign, asked one of his generals, "Can you give me a proof that the Bible is the Word of God?" He replied, "Your Majesty, the Jew. Against all historical precedence, he has survived centuries of dispersion and yet has remained a distinct people—a nation in exile—though scattered over the entire world and terribly persecuted, just as the Hebrew prophets predicted he would be, patiently waiting for his promised return to the land of his fathers."

NAPOLEON BONAPARTE, 1798

The roots of the Arab-Israeli conflict occurred more than 4000 years ago. A man was called for a special mission that would forever change the course of human history. It is impossible to understand the present Middle East crisis without knowledge of exactly what happened then and why.

This all began at a time when all nations were determined to push the knowledge of the one true God out of their culture and memory. The Bible records that because of this, God chose a man for the purpose of creating a special nation. God's purpose for this nation was to preserve a true revelation about Himself, to reach out to the world through it and ultimately to provide salvation for all mankind.

The Bible records how God chose a man named Abram, whom He later renamed Abraham, from Ur of the Chaldeans and made a special covenant with him and his descendants to facilitate this purpose.

In this covenant, God's plan for all mankind is laid out in broad outline. In terms of its effect upon the history of mankind, nothing else can compare with it. It is truly amazing, but the rest of the Bible is commentary on the promises it contains. To put its importance into perspective, the main focus of the Bible message from Genesis chapter twelve to Acts chapter two are the recipients of its promises—Abraham and his descendants.

The Irrevocable Covenant

The covenant is formed around God's declaration of four direct and three understood "I WILLS". This is the God of the Bible's consistent formula for expressing an unconditional promise. The one requirement on Abraham's part was to by faith leave his country, his home, and his relatives to travel to a land that God would show him.

In response to that faith, God promised Abraham the following:

Now the Lord had said to Abram:
"Get out of your country,
From your family and from your father's house,
To a land that I will show you.
I WILL make you a great nation;
I WILL bless you
And [I WILL] make your name great;
And you shall be a blessing.
I WILL bless those who bless you,
And I WILL curse him who curses you;
And in you all the families of the earth
**   shall be blessed."** [1]

So much is contained in these few words that they must be carefully analyzed.

THE PROMISE OF A NATION
"I WILL make you a great nation . . ."

This implicitly contained the promise of a son through whom this Nation would be created. It also implicitly promised the land to which he had come, since you can't have a nation without a land.

There was one big problem—Abraham and his wife were childless. Yet everything God promised Abraham depended upon him having a son. Now since he was 75 years old and his wife was 65 years old, Abraham understood that it would take some kind of Divine intervention for him to have a son. This "complication" resulted in a lapse of Abraham's faith.

THE PROMISES OF SPECIAL PERSONAL BLESSINGS
"I WILL bless you and make your name great;
and you shall be a blessing . . ."

God promised to bless Abraham in three ways: (1) God blessed

---

1. Genesis 12:1–3, emphasis added.

him with special protection, great wealth, vibrant health even into old age, and made him successful in all his dealings. (2) God promised to make his name great. His name has been reverenced all over the world for more than 4000 years. He is recognized as a spiritual father by three of the world's major religions—Judaism, Christianity and Islam. God promised to make him a blessing. Untold millions of people have recognized him as the father of their faith. The example of Abraham's faith, permanently recorded in the eternal Word of God, has been a blessing to countless millions throughout history.

Promises That Anticipated Anti-Semitism
THE PROMISES OF DIVINE PROTECTION
"I WILL bless those who bless you,
And I WILL curse him who curses you ..."

These "I WILLS" anticipated that Abraham and his descendants would be the objects of special attack. In view of their special mission of redemption to the world, it is only logical that they would be singled out as prime targets by the devil. Anti-Semitism has been a relentless fact of history.

Abraham and his Divinely chosen line of descendants through Isaac and Jacob have been consistently persecuted. There is a mystical quality behind the intensity of hatred toward the Israelites. This is especially true of the descendants of the Southern Kingdom that is composed of the tribes of Judah, Benjamin and Levi. They were first called "Jews" while in Babylonian captivity. The name "Jew" was derived from the name of their geographical origin, Judea. The Jews have been singled out for special hatred since they were driven into global exile after the destruction of Israel in 70 A.D. The name "Jew" has come to be indiscriminately applied to survivors of all twelve tribes of Israelites in recent centuries.

Only a person who understands the one the Bible calls **"the god of this age"**[2] can begin to understand this mystery. Any objective

---

2. 2 Corinthians 4:3.

study of the irrational outbreaks of hatred all over the world toward the Israelites—their mindless slaughter in every century—will reveal that there is a malevolent spiritual force behind it all.

THE PROMISE OF BLESSING UPON ALL WHO BLESS ISRAEL
"I WILL bless those who bless you . . ."

Individuals, groups and nations that have sought to help Abraham and his descendants in their times of need have all been blessed by God. The United States has received, helped and protected the dispersed Israelites. The US has stood for Israel's survival as a nation from its re-birth in 1948. I believe this is one of the main reasons God has so blessed America. But as we will see, our attitude toward Israel is changing, to the peril of our nation.

THE PROMISE OF JUDGMENT UPON ALL WHO CURSE (HARM) ISRAEL
"I WILL curse him who curses you . . ."

Since God chose to create the nation of Israel for the special mission of redeeming the rest of mankind, beware of mistreating or harming them. God's promise of protection to Abraham and his seed serves as a warning to the nations or gentiles; **"I WILL curse him who curses you . . ."** All attacks upon Israelites will ultimately bring retribution from God. When gentiles attack them, they are attacking God's chosen instruments of their own redemption.

This promise of God's protection was confirmed by Isaac to his son, Jacob, when he passed on the Divine blessing to him, **". . . Cursed be those who curse you, and blessed be those who bless you."**[3]

Almost four hundred years later, God made even the apostate prophet Balaam pronounce this solemn warning to King Balak, who had hired him to curse the Nation of Israel.

---

3. Genesis 27:29b.

". . . How shall I curse, whom God has not cursed? And how can I denounce, whom the LORD has not denounced? . . . BLESSED IS EVERYONE who blesses you, and CURSED IS EVERYONE who curses you."[4]

This account is extremely important. These verses prove that the promise of God's protection included all the descendants of Abraham, Isaac and Jacob.

Just to illustrate how seriously God takes this promise, the Hebrew prophet Zechariah, 1600 years after Abraham, warns of the Messiah's first action when He comes to set up God's Kingdom on earth:

"For thus says the Lord of hosts, 'After glory He has sent me against the nations which plunder you, FOR HE WHO TOUCHES YOU, TOUCHES THE APPLE OF HIS EYE. For behold, I will wave My hand over them, so that they will be plunder for their slaves.' Then you will know that the Lord of hosts has sent Me. "Sing for joy and be glad, O daughter of Zion; for behold I am coming and I will dwell in your midst," declares the Lord. "And many nations will join themselves to the Lord in that day and will become My people. Then I will dwell in your midst, and you will know that the Lord of hosts has sent Me to you." And the Lord will possess Judah as His portion in the holy land, and will again choose Jerusalem."[5]

We know this event as the Second Coming of Jesus the Messiah. It is certain that this refers to the time of the second coming because the Messiah sets up His throne in Jerusalem and dwells among His people. According this prophecy, the first thing He will do is judge all of the Gentiles who have mistreated His people, Israel.

Much more will be said about this important subject later.

---

4. Numbers 23:8 and 24:9b, emphasis added.

5. Zechariah 2:8–12, emphasis added.

THE PROMISE OF MANKIND'S SALVATION
"And in you all the families of the earth shall be blessed."

The last promise is the most important. Abraham and his descendants will be the vessels through which all the peoples of the earth will be blessed. The literal translation is, **"And in you I WILL bless all the families of the earth."**

This promise reveals the main purpose for which Abraham and his descendants were chosen. They are to be the vessels through which God will reach out to the world with his plan of salvation.

In embryonic form, this promise predicts the provision of salvation for the whole world through one of Abraham's seed. It reveals that the ultimate purpose of God though Abraham and his seed is redemptive.

As the Bible develops and adds to this promise of blessing the people of the world, four reasons for why God chose and created Israel are discernable:

- First, they are to receive, write and preserve the Word of God. As the Apostle Paul testified, **". . . they were entrusted with the oracles of God."** [6]

- Second, the way God deals with Israel in response to their faith or lack of faith is a living historical lesson about God's character. The way God dealt with Israel as a nation teaches principles of how He deals with the individual who believes in Him. [7]

- Third, they are to be the physical race through which the Messiah, the Savior of the world would be born. Isaiah predicted the mission of this Messiah, **"It is too small a thing that You should be My Servant to raise up the tribes of Jacob, and to restore the preserved ones of Israel; I will also make**

---

6. Romans 3:2

7. An example of how the Spirit of God uses historical accounts of how God responded to Israel's faith and lack of faith is in Hebrews 3:7 through 4:13. He quotes from Israel's history as a basis to teach Christians about believing God's promises today.

You a light to the Gentiles so that My salvation may reach to the end of the earth."[8]

- Fourth, they are called to spread the message of the true God and His salvation to the world.

The Only Land-Deed God Ever Gave

God expanded upon the original covenant with another essential covenant. It concerns the land on which He would establish the nation of Abraham and his descendants. There are several promises made about this land that together carefully spell out: (1) to whom it is given (2) its borders (3) conditions of ownership (4) duration of its ownership. God foreknew the great troubles that Israel would encounter concerning the rights to their land throughout history—especially in the "Last Days." So He stated the terms of their "Title Deed" to the land in a comprehensive covenant, backed by His own oath.

As mentioned above, the one condition for Abraham to fulfill was to leave his country and relatives and go to the land that God would show him. So after Abraham obeyed this order, all of the promises that followed were unconditional.

This is what God promised Abraham shortly after He gave him the first covenant,

> "And the Lord appeared to Abram and said, 'To your descendants I WILL give this land.'" And, ". . . for all the land which you see, I WILL GIVE IT TO YOU AND TO YOUR DESCENDANTS FOREVER. And I will make your descendants as the dust of the earth; so that if anyone can number the dust of the earth, then your descendants can also be numbered. Arise, walk about the land through its length and breadth; for I will give it to you."[9]

It is very important to note the features of this covenant God

---

8. Isaiah 49:6.

9. Genesis 12:7 and 13:15–17, emphasis added.

made with Abraham. They have a direct bearing on the controversy raging in the Middle East today. Note first that it is given not only to Abraham, but also to his descendants.

Second, it is an unconditional covenant. God swore, **"I WILL"** do this without attaching any conditions upon the recipients. Third, it is **"FOREVER"**, thus the behavior of Abraham or his descendants cannot break its ultimate everlasting fulfillment.

Boundaries of the Deeded Land

The border of the land that is to be ultimately possessed by the Abraham's descendants is spelled out very specifically in the next expansion of the land covenant. Something else is added that is unique in God's dealing with mankind.

After the above covenants, Abraham believed the LORD concerning a promised son who would come from his own body, and offspring as numerous as the stars of heaven. But he still wanted more assurance regarding the possession of the Promised Land. So he asked, **"O Sovereign LORD, how can I know that I will gain possession of it [the land]?"** [10]

God's response is one of the greatest demonstrations of how patient and gracious He is with mankind. God chose to accommodate Abraham's continuing need for strong reassurance. He did this by performing a strange covenant-making ritual that, in the culture of that time, was the most solemn and binding known to man. Here is the account of how God reconfirmed to Abraham the title deed to the land and its boundaries. It is so important that I am quoting the ceremony in its entirety:

> **"So the LORD said to him, "Bring me a heifer, a goat and a ram, each three years old, along with a dove and a young pigeon."**
>
> **Abram brought all these to him, cut them in two and arranged the halves opposite each other; the birds, how-**

---

10. Genesis 15:8.

ever, he did not cut in half. Then birds of prey came down on the carcasses, but Abram drove them away.

As the sun was setting, Abram fell into a deep sleep, and a thick and dreadful darkness came over him. Then the LORD said to him, "Know for certain that your descendants will be strangers in a country not their own, and they will be enslaved and mistreated four hundred years. But I will punish the nation they serve as slaves, and afterward they will come out with great possessions. You, however, will go to your fathers in peace and be buried at a good old age. In the fourth generation your descendants will come back here, for the sin of the Amorites has not yet reached its full measure."

When the sun had set and darkness had fallen, a smoking firepot with a blazing torch appeared and passed between the pieces. On that day the LORD made a covenant with Abram and said, "To your descendants I give this land, from the river of Egypt to the great river, the Euphrates—the land of the Kenites, Kenizzites, Kadmonites, Hittites, Perizzites, Rephaites, Amorites, Canaanites, Girgashites and Jebusites." [11]

This passage gives important details concerning the irrevocable nature of the covenant. This strange ritual gets at the heart of the meaning of the Hebrew word for covenant. It comes from the verb *barath*, which means, "to cut." In Hebrew the expression for making a covenant is "to cut a covenant." The Hebrew scholar F. Delitzsch writes concerning this ritual:

> The proceeding corresponded rather to the custom, prevalent in many ancient nations, of slaughtering animals when concluding a covenant, and after dividing them into pieces, of laying the pieces opposite to one another, that the persons making the covenant might pass between them . . . God condescended to follow the custom of the Chaldeans, that He might in the most solemn manner confirm His oath to Abram the Chaldean. [12]

11. Genesis 15:9–19 (NIV).

12. C. F. Keil and F. Delitzsch, *Commentary of the Old Testament* (Grand Rapids, MI: William. B. Eerdmans Publishing Co., reprinted 1983), vol. 1, p. 214.

This reveals much about the character of God. Certainly it shows that He is gracious and considerate of our human limitations. It demonstrates that He takes into account our degree of maturity and knowledge of Him in His treatment of us.

An Oath That Can Never Be Broken

As the custom dictated, Abram laid the sacrifice halves opposite each other, making a path in the middle for those making the covenant to walk. The parties would then hold hands and walk together between the sacrifices, taking an oath on the terms of the covenant. They would then swear an oath that the one who breaks the covenant is to be hewn in pieces as the sacrifices had been. We are talking serious covenant making here.

But in this case, a most unusual thing happened. Abraham was put into a deep sleep and shown a vision of God walking alone between the sacrifices and swearing an oath by Himself that He would give the land with its specific borders to Abraham and his descendants as an everlasting possession.

For God to give His Word in a promise is enough to make it unbreakable. But God swore an oath by Himself that He would fulfill this promise concerning the land. Thus by two immutable things, His Word and His oath, it is made certain beyond all things. *So let all who contest Israel's right to that land today beware.*

Why the Canaanites Would Be Destroyed

A prophecy was also given to Abraham as to when his descendants would first take possession of the land. It would be after they spent 400 years in the land of Egypt. The reason for the delay was twofold. First, it was because Abraham's descendants had to grow in sufficient numbers to be able to take over the land.

And second, because the sin of the present inhabitants had not yet reached the full measure of iniquity worthy of their destruction. God graciously gave them 400 more years to repent, which they never did. They only got worse, burning their own children alive as a sacrifice to demon idols. When God later brought the Israelites back from Egypt, the minds of all the residents of Canaan had become utterly perverted beyond reformation. They were like a cancer that had to be exorcised before their perversion infected the rest of society.

Abraham's Understanding of the Covenant

How Abraham understood this covenant is revealed in a later statement he made to his steward when he sent him after a wife for his son Isaac,

> **"The LORD, the God of heaven, who brought me out of my father's household and my native land and who spoke to me and promised me on oath, saying, 'To your offspring I WILL give this land'—he will send his angel before you so that you can get a wife for my son from there. If the woman is unwilling to come back with you, then you will be released from this oath of mine. Only do not take my son back there."** [13]

In the light of the above Scripture, to say, as some teachers within Christendom do, that there was no unconditional covenant made with Abraham's descendants is to accuse God of willfully deceiving Abraham. And it would be even more ludicrous to suppose that the LORD would record Abraham's wrong understanding of this covenant if in fact it was wrong. God warned that He would discipline the Israelites, but never disown them.

How Anti-Semitism Began

There are false teachers within the Church today who would deny that the Israelites have a right to the land of their forefathers. They are known by such titles as "Dominionists", "Preterists", "Amillennialists" or "Postmillennialists".

---

13. Genesis 24:7–8.

What is common to all of these theological systems is that they allegorize all unfulfilled Bible prophecies and covenants—especially those that apply to the future of the descendants of Abraham, Isaac and Jacob. They say that the covenants were "conditional", and therefore were canceled by Israel's rejection of the Messiah, Jesus. They teach that Israel has no future in God's plan as a distinct people and nation. They teach that the Church inherited all of these covenants and promises when Israel rejected their Messiah, Jesus.

In other words, they believe that the Church has now become "Israel" in place of the literal, physical descendants to whom the promises were exclusively made. This is called "Replacement Theology". Augustine laid the groundwork for this teaching in the 5th century A.D. He taught that the Church had become Israel and was now God's Kingdom on earth. This became the rationale for the "Conquistadors" to conquer and pillage the Americas in the name of the Roman Catholic Church. It also was the philosophy that set up the "Holy Roman Empire" over Europe. This resulted in such shameful atrocities as the Crusades and the Inquisitions in "the name of Jesus". These actions violated the most basic teachings of Jesus Christ. The Knights of Europe, under the orders of the Popes, slaughtered tens of thousands of innocent people, particularly the Jews.

The New Testament Confirms This Title Deed

In the 1st century Roman Church, some Christians were inclined to turn against the Jews and think they had permanently replaced them in God's plan. So this is God's answer to that error:

> **"For I do not want you, brethren, to be uninformed of this mystery, lest you be wise in your own estimation, that a partial hardening has happened to Israel UNTIL the fullness** [full number] **of the Gentiles has come in; and thus all Israel will be saved; just as it is written, "The Deliverer will come from Zion, He will remove ungodli-**

ness from Jacob." And, "This is My covenant with them, When I take away their sins." From the standpoint of the gospel they are enemies for your sake, but from the standpoint of God's choice they are beloved for the sake of the fathers; for the gifts and the calling of God are IRREVOCABLE." [14]

The Apostle Paul reveals that the present rejection of Israel is not total, nor is it final. It is only temporary *until* the full number of Gentiles is saved. Then he quotes specific promises of God that guarantee that **"all Israel will be saved when the Deliverer** [the Messiah Jesus] **comes from Zion** [in the Second Coming].**"**

The Epistle to the Romans carefully defines in Chapter Nine that **"true Israel"** is composed of the physical descendants of Abraham, Isaac and Jacob who also believe in God's provision of salvation. They are called **"the believing remnant."** As it is written:

"And Isaiah cries out concerning Israel, 'Though the number of the sons of Israel be as the sand of the sea, IT IS THE REMNANT THAT WILL BE SAVED; for the Lord will execute His word upon the earth, thoroughly and quickly.' " [15]

The practice of allegorizing these specific promises, which started with the 5th century theologian Augustine, became the foundation of anti-Semitism in the Church. Sadly, anti-Semitism spread from the Church to the rest of the world.

If the Curses Are Literal, the Promises Are Too

Moses predicted two destructions of Israel and two dispersions from their land. It is amazing that he predicted this just before they first took possession of the land.

---

14. Romans 11:25–29, emphasis added (vv. 26–27 quotes Isaiah 59:20–21 and Jeremiah 31:33–34).
15. Romans 9:27–28, emphasis added. (Quotes Isaiah 10:22–23).

The reason for their national destruction is given:

"All these curses will come upon you. They will pursue you and overtake you until you are destroyed, because you did not obey the LORD your God and observe the commands and decrees he gave you. They will be a sign and a wonder to you and your descendants forever." [16]

Moses then predicted the first destruction,

"The LORD will bring a nation against you from far away, from the ends of the earth, like an eagle swooping down, a nation whose language you will not understand, a fierce-looking nation without respect for the old or pity for the young." [17]

This was fulfilled by the Babylonian destruction led by Nebuchadnezzar at the end of the 7th century BC.

Moses also predicted the second, more severe destruction and dispersion:

"Then the LORD will scatter you among all nations, from one end of the earth to the other. There you will worship other gods—gods of wood and stone, which neither you nor your fathers have known. Among those nations you will find no repose, no resting place for the sole of your foot. There the LORD will give you an anxious mind, eyes weary with longing, and a despairing heart. You will live in constant suspense, filled with dread both night and day, never sure of your life. In the morning you will say, 'If only it were evening!' and in the evening, 'If only it were morning!'—because of the terror that will fill your hearts and the sights that your eyes will see." [18]

This terrible catastrophe took place in 70 A.D. when Titus and the Roman Tenth Legion destroyed Judah and Jerusalem and drove the survivors into exile. This dispersion lasted until it began to be reversed with the re-birth of the state of Israel in June of 1948.

---

16. Deuteronomy 28:45–46 (NIV).

17. Deuteronomy 28:49–50 (NIV).

18. Deuteronomy 28:64–68 (NIV).

Predictions Of Israel's Second And Final Restoration

The following predictions cut to the heart of the current Arab-Israeli conflict. They show that the "title deed to the land of Israel" was never revoked. It is still binding on the basis of the Divine oath by which it was originally given. The Muslims absolutely reject this. So their current attempts to drive Israel out of the Holy Land are in direct defiance of God.

Moses, at the end of the same message, made this predictions of ultimate restoration:

> **"When all these blessings and curses I have set before you come upon you and you take them to heart wherever the LORD your God disperses you among the nations, and when you and your children return to the LORD your God and obey him with all your heart and with all your soul according to everything I command you today, then the LORD your God will restore your fortunes and have compassion on you and gather you again from all the nations where he scattered you. Even if you have been banished to the most distant land under the heavens, from there the LORD your God will gather you and bring you back. He will bring you to the land that belonged to your fathers, and you will take possession of it. He will make you more prosperous and numerous than your fathers."** [19]

It is important to note that God does not say "if" but "when" throughout this prediction. This is because God views the repentance as certain, since He will cause it to happen. It is also very clear that God addresses this promise to the believing remnant of the physical descendants of Abraham, Isaac and Jacob—not to some allegorical offspring in the Church.

Ezekiel also speaks of this final restoration from the worldwide Roman dispersion:

> **"This is what the Sovereign LORD says: I will deal**

---

19. Deuteronomy 30:1–5 (NIV).

with you as you deserve, because you have despised my oath by breaking the covenant. YET I WILL REMEMBER THE COVENANT I MADE WITH YOU IN THE DAYS OF YOUR YOUTH, AND I WILL ESTABLISH AN EVERLASTING COVENANT WITH YOU. Then you will remember your ways and be ashamed when you receive your sisters, both those who are older than you and those who are younger. I will give them to you as daughters, but not on the basis of my covenant with you. So I will establish my covenant with you, and you will know that I am the LORD. Then, when I make atonement for you for all you have done, you will remember and be ashamed and never again open your mouth because of your humiliation, declares the Sovereign LORD." [20]

Note that God anticipated that Israel would despise His oath and break the Mosaic covenant. He warns that He will discipline them, as they deserve. Yet despite all they will do, He still promises that He will fulfill to them the covenant made with their fathers.

There is no excuse for those who call themselves Christian to deny the clear, simple, literal statements of God's Word about the Israelites' covenant rights. The traditional prophetic view of many mainline churches that are based on unwarranted allegorical interpretations of these passages has caused great chaos and suffering to the descendants of Abraham, Isaac and Jacob.

David Levi and Isaac Da Costa, who were Christian Biblical scholars of the 19th century, clearly point out a great inconsistency in the interpretation of Biblical Prophecy concerning the nation of Israel by the theological systems known as Preterists, Amillennialists, Post Millennialists, et al.:

> What can be more absurd than to explain the prophecies, which foretell the calamity to befall the Jews, in a literal sense, and then those, which bespeak their future blessing, in a mystical and spiritual sense? [21]

---

20. Ezekiel 16:59–63 (NIV), emphasis added.

21. David Levi, quoted by Nathaniel West, *The Thousand Years in Both Testaments*, (New York, N.Y.: Fleming Revel, 1880), p. 462

The Specific Prediction of Final Restoration To The Land

Ezekiel predicts Israel's final restoration to the land and rebirth as a nation in the "Last Days". It is imperative to note the sequence of this prophecy. It clearly shows that God will restore the Israelites to the land and cause them to be reborn as a nation BEFORE they repent and believe in their true Messiah:

> "Therefore, say to the house of Israel, 'Thus says the Lord God, "IT IS NOT FOR YOUR SAKE, O HOUSE OF ISRAEL, THAT I AM ABOUT TO ACT, BUT FOR MY HOLY NAME, which you have profaned among the nations where you went."' 'And I will vindicate the holiness of My great name which has been profaned among the nations, which you have profaned in their midst. Then the nations will know that I am the Lord,' declares the Lord God, 'when I prove Myself holy among you in their sight. For I WILL take you from the nations, gather you from all the lands, and BRING YOU INTO YOUR OWN LAND.
>
> "'THEN I WILL sprinkle clean water on you, and you will be clean; I WILL cleanse you from all your filthiness and from all your idols. Moreover, I WILL give you a new heart and put a new spirit within you; and I WILL remove the heart of stone from your flesh and give you a heart of flesh. And I WILL put My Spirit within you and cause you to walk in My statutes, and you will be careful to observe My ordinances. And you will live in the land that I gave to your forefathers; so you will be My people, and I WILL be your God.'"[22]

This prophecy clearly adds a new dimension to all of the predictions about Israel's restoration to the land. It emphasizes that it is not being done because they deserve it. They are returned to the land and reborn as a nation BEFORE they are cleansed and reborn spiritually.

---

22. Ezekiel 36:22–28, emphasis added.

The paragraph beginning with **"THEN I WILL"** clearly marks out the sequence of events. It is only after they are returned to the land that they are brought to spiritual restoration. In every way the prophecy declares that all of this will be done by sovereign, unconditional acts of God despite the unworthiness of the Israelites. God swears an oath that He will do all of this with seven sovereign **"I WILLs"**.

Ezekiel's Prophetic Outline Of Today's Events

Ezekiel lays out more clearly than any other Prophet the sequence of events in the Last Days. He shows that restored Israel is the key to all last days' prophecy.

Ezekiel 36 emphasizes the miracle of the land's restoration when God returns His people to it. The prophecy focuses on the desolate condition of the land that the surrounding nations (which are all Muslim today) have brought upon it. God warns of terrible judgment upon these Muslim nations who have **"taken His Land."** The fact that it is God's land is emphasized several times.

Ezekiel 37 emphasizes the miracle of returning the dispersed Israelites from all the nations where they have been scattered for centuries. Ezekiel describes this miraculous national rebirth of the people in an allegory about disjointed skeletons lying in a desert full of open graves. He interprets the scattered bones as the whole house of Israel. He reveals that the open graves are the nations where the people have been scattered. The miracle of Israel's national rebirth is illustrated by all of the bones coming out of the graves and joining together. Then sinews, muscle and flesh come upon them—and finally, breath is breathed into them. They then stand up as a mighty army. But they are still not reborn spiritually.

Ezekiel 38 reveals the momentous event of history that will finally bring the Israelites to faith in their true Messiah. It will be a massive invasion against them led by a mighty nation to their extreme north. This northern commander (who can only be

Russian since they are the only nation to Israel's extreme north) will lead a confederacy of people who are all today Muslim. Chief among those named is Persia, or modern Iran.

How this all turns out will be developed in later chapters. But suffice it to say, the scenario spelled out here is all in place in our current events.

The main point of these chapters is that they show that once Israel is restored, it will never be destroyed and dispersed again. Even though Ezekiel does predict that Israel will go through a war so intense that all hope of survival will be lost. It is at this point that great numbers of Israelites will turn to their true Messiah and believe in Him. He will then miraculously deliver them and set up the promised Kingdom of God on earth.

The prophet Zechariah foresaw this climactic event over 2,500 years ago. He quotes the Lord directly:

> **"And I will pour out on the house of David and on the inhabitants of Jerusalem, the Spirit of grace and supplication, so that THEY WILL LOOK ON ME WHOM THEY HAVE PIERCED; and they will mourn for Him, as one mourns for an only son, and they will weep bitterly over Him, like the bitter weeping over a first-born."** [23]

There is only one time in history that Israel pierced their God, though they didn't know he was their God. It was when Jesus of Nazareth was crucified for claiming to be who He really is, the Messiah and Savior of Israel. No wonder those who repent and recognize Him will weep. God then promises:

> **"In that day a fountain will be opened for the house of David and for the inhabitants of Jerusalem, for sin and for impurity."** [24]

---

23. Zechariah 12:10, emphasis added.
24. Zechariah 13:1.

How These Covenants Effect Today

The creation of a special people with unconditional promises of an everlasting title deed to specific land in the Middle East has brought unique problems to the world.

The problem was greatly intensified by, first, their destruction and 2000 year dispersion throughout the whole world; and second, by the fact they survived as a distinct people and returned to claim their ancient homeland again in the midst of the Muslims who have possessed it for centuries.

There is one more unique problem that was created by these covenants that will bring the present world order to a catastrophic end. This will be the subject of a future chapter. But first, it must be established just exactly who are the inheritors of the Covenants made to Abraham.

CHAPTER THREE

Who Is Abraham's True Son?

God also said to Moses, "Say to the Israelites, 'The LORD[1], the God of your fathers—the God of Abraham, the God of Isaac and the God of Jacob —has sent me to you.' This is my name forever, the name by which I am to be remembered from generation to generation."

EXODUS 3:15 (NIV)

---

1. The Hebrew for LORD sounds like and may be derived from the Hebrew for I AM ["Yahweh"], which was just revealed as God's special name to Moses in the previous verse. In most English Bibles, the translation of the name, Yahweh or Jehovah, is "LORD" in all capital letters.

For some of my readers, even raising this question may seem ridiculous. But there have been those who have tried to rewrite Biblical history and say that the covenants made with Abraham were not given to his son Isaac and his grandson Jacob.

This has become especially critical in modern times. The Muslims have vehemently argued that neither Isaac or Jacob were the chosen line of descendants to whom the covenants were confirmed. Later in this book, I will lay out the teachings of the Muslims and the Koran on this issue and why they dispute what is written the Bible. But in this chapter we'll look at what the Bible says and how it has been confirmed in history. It is imperative to be familiar with this aspect of Biblical record. For as we will see, it's absolutely necessary to learn the facts traced out here if we are to understand the real dynamics behind the present Arab-Israeli conflict that troubles our world.

The Miracle Son

Abraham was 75 and Sarah, his wife, was 65 when God swore to him the covenants outlined in the last chapter. As I noted, Abraham knew that all of the promises he received required him to have a son. And since they were childless at such an advanced age, he knew that it would take a miracle for this to happen.

When Abraham turned 86 (11 years after God unconditionally promised to give him a son), he stumbled in his faith and tried to help God fulfill the promise about a son. He applied the old saying, "God helps those who help themselves." But that is not a verse in the Bible. In fact it's the opposite of what the Bible teaches. God helps those who recognize that they are helpless and then trust God to do what is humanly impossible.

This episode apparently short-circuited God's work in Abraham's life for a long period. It wasn't until Abraham reached 99 (13 years later) that God appeared to him and reconfirmed all the covenants. This is the occasion when God changed his name from Abram, which means *father of high places*, to Abraham, which means *father of many peoples or nations.*[2]

Shortly after this revelation, three extraordinary men appeared to Abraham. Apparently they had a heavenly bearing and appearance because Abraham gave them the reverence he reserved only for Deity. He bowed down before them and begged them to stay for dinner.

During the course of the meal, it became obvious to Abraham that the three heavenly beings were the LORD Himself. It was at this time the LORD specifically promised that at the same time next year, Abraham's wife would bear him a son. Now Sarah by that time would be 90, barren and well beyond the age of child bearing. And Abraham would be 100, likewise beyond the age of fathering children.

As a matter of fact, when Sarah heard this promise (she was inside the tent and out of sight) she began to laugh to herself in disbelief. At this point the supernatural powers of the three men began to be revealed. They said to Abraham, "Why did Sarah, your wife, laugh?" Since she was out of sight and had not made a sound, Abraham exclaimed she didn't laugh.

Here is how the Bible records the incident:

> **So Sarah laughed to herself as she thought, "After I am worn out and my master is old, will I now have this pleasure?" Then the LORD said to Abraham, "Why did Sarah laugh and say, 'Will I really have a child, now that I am old?' Is anything too hard for the LORD? I will return to you at the appointed time next year and Sarah will have a son." Sarah was afraid, so she lied and said, "I did not laugh." But he said, "Yes, you did laugh."[3]**

This is one of those wonderful times when God shows His sense of humor. God ordered them to name the miracle child, Isaac, or *Yitzak* in Hebrew, which means "laughter". So every time

---

2. Genesis 17.

3. Genesis 18:12–15 (NIV).

Sarah called her son, "Laughter", she was reminded that she didn't believe God would give her a son.[4]

The Covenants Confirmed to Isaac

Abraham was overjoyed when Sarah bore him Isaac. But Isaac's birth presented some complications. Abraham already had a son, Ishmael, through his Egyptian handmaid. Ishmael was technically his first-born—a fact that is greatly stressed by Arabs and Muslims. I will expand on this more in the next chapter.

When God restated His promise to Abraham regarding Sarah giving birth to his true heir, he reacted in a strange way:

> **God also said to Abraham, "As for Sarai your wife, you are no longer to call her Sarai; her name will be Sarah. I will bless her and will surely give you a son by her. I will bless her so that she will be the mother of nations; kings of peoples will come from her." Abraham fell face down; he laughed and said to himself, "Will a son be born to a man a hundred years old? Will Sarah bear a child at the age of ninety?" And Abraham said to God, "If only Ishmael might live under your blessing!" Then God said, "Yes, but your wife Sarah will bear you a son, and you will call him Isaac. *I will establish my covenant with him as an everlasting covenant for his descendants after him.*[5]**

So it was made very clear who was the chosen one through whom the covenants were given and through whom God would work.

Later, when Abraham made arrangements to find Isaac an approved wife, he reconfirmed his understanding as to who was the chosen son:

> **The servant asked him, "What if the woman is unwilling**

---

4. This is theologically a very important chapter. The three men are called God. The sovereign actions of God are attributed to the three equally. So here we have the first clear revelation that God is three persons within the One Godhead. They exist as co-equal and co-eternal beings in one Godhead. The mystery is how One God exists in three persons.

5. Genesis 17:15–19 (NIV), emphasis added.

> to come back with me to this land? Shall I then take your son back to the country you came from?" "Make sure that you do not take my son back there," Abraham said. "The LORD, the God of heaven, who brought me out of my father's household and my native land and who spoke to me and promised me on oath, saying, *'To your offspring I will give this land'*—he will send his angel before you so that you can get a wife for my son from there. If the woman is unwilling to come back with you, then you will be released from this oath of mine. Only do not take my son back there."[6]

Here, Abraham clearly states that the land covenant belongs to Isaac. He is adamant that under no circumstances was his son to return to the land God had told him to leave in order to qualify for the covenant blessings.

When Abraham made the final disposition of his estate and the blessings of the promised covenants, the Bible records, **"Abraham left everything he owned to Isaac."**[7]

The Covenants Confirmed to Jacob

This is the Biblical record of Abraham's chosen descendents:

> This is the account of Abraham's son Isaac. Abraham became the father of Isaac, and Isaac was forty years old when he married Rebekah daughter of Bethuel the Aramean from Paddan Aram (That is, Northwest Mesopotamia) and sister of Laban the Aramean.
>
> Isaac prayed to the LORD on behalf of his wife, because she was barren. The LORD answered his prayer, and his wife Rebekah became pregnant. The babies jostled each other within her, and she said, "Why is this happening to me?" So she went to inquire of the LORD. The LORD said to her, "Two nations are in your womb, and two peoples from within you will be separated; one people

---

6. Genesis 24:5–8 (NIV), emphasis added.
7. Genesis 25:5 (NIV).

will be stronger than the other, and the older will serve the younger."

When the time came for her to give birth, there were twin boys in her womb. The first to come out was red, and his whole body was like a hairy garment; so they named him Esau. (Esau may mean hairy; he was also called Edom, which means red.) **After this, his brother came out, with his hand grasping Esau's heel; so he was named Jacob.** (Jacob means figuratively, *he cheats*) **Isaac was sixty years old when Rebekah gave birth to them.**[8]

Talk about trouble, these boys fought each other while still in the womb—and it progressed from there.

As the boys grew up, there were all the makings of a family civil war. Isaac favored Esau, because he was the "outdoorsy" type and a great hunter. He used to bring Isaac's favorite game home and make him a spicy stew. Esau was also a very aggressive warrior-type man. Today we would call him, "a man's man."

On the other hand, Rebekah loved Jacob. Jacob was a peaceful and contemplative man who loved to be around home. He apparently also loved spiritual things, for he wanted the blessings of the firstborn, which were primarily spiritual.

In the course of events, Jacob made some lentil stew about the time that Esau came in famished after a long hunt. Esau smelled the food and told Jacob, **"Give me some of that red stuff, for I am famished."**

Then Jacob made a very shrewd deal with Esau:

Jacob replied, "First sell me your birthright." "Look, I am about to die," Esau said. "What good is the birthright to me?" But Jacob said, "Swear to me first." So he swore an oath to him, selling his birthright to Jacob. Then Jacob gave Esau some bread and some lentil stew. He ate and

---

8. Genesis 25:19–26 (NIV).

drank, and then got up and left. So Esau despised his birthright.[9]

This was the most expensive stew in history. Surely Esau was aware of the spiritual significance of the covenants God made with his grandfather, Abraham. If he were a believer in the God of Abraham, he would never have dealt so flippantly with such a high privilege of being chosen by God as His representative on earth. This is why God later made this pronouncement, **"Jacob I have loved; But Esau I have hated . . ."**[10]

Apparently Esau conveniently forgot about this transaction, because when it came time for Isaac to confer the rights and covenants of the firstborn, Esau expected them to be his.

But Rebekah and Jacob devised a little conspiracy to make sure that did not happen. Isaac at the time of his death had gone blind. So Rebekah put Esau's clothes on Jacob to make him smell like Esau. She also tied goat hide on the back of his hands and around his neck so that he would feel hairy like Esau. Then she made Isaac's favorite savory stew and had Jacob take it in to Isaac.

When Isaac smelled Esau's clothes on Jacob, hugged his hairy neck and held his hands, he was convinced that he was Esau. So he swore this oath to him:

> **"See, the smell of my son is like the smell of a field which the LORD has blessed; Now may God give you of the dew of heaven, and of the fatness of the earth, and an abundance of grain and new wine;**
>
> **"May peoples serve you, and nations bow down to you; be master of your brothers, and may your mother's sons bow down to you.**
>
> **"Cursed be those who curse you, and blessed be those who bless you."**[11]

---

9. Genesis 25:31–34 (NIV).

10. Malachi 1:2–3 (NKJV).

11. Genesis 27:27–29 (NKJV).

Even though Isaac and Esau discovered that same day that Jacob had tricked them, the oath was still binding. All the rights of the firstborn had been irrevocably conferred upon Jacob by an oath to God.

Esau became enraged. So Rebekah thought up another scheme to get Jacob out of harm's way. She went to Isaac and told him that her whole life would be ruined if Jacob married one of the local girls who were idol worshippers. So Isaac called Jacob in and commanded him,

> **"You shall not take a wife from the daughters of Canaan. Arise, go to Paddan-Aram, to the house of Bethuel your mother's father; and from there take to yourself a wife from the daughters of Laban your mother's brother. And may God Almighty bless you and make you fruitful and multiply you, that you may become a company of peoples. May He also give you the blessing of Abraham, to you and to your descendants with you; that you may possess the land of your sojournings, which God gave to Abraham." Then Isaac sent Jacob away, and he went to Paddan-Aram to Laban, son of Bethuel the Aramean, the brother of Rebekah, the mother of Jacob and Esau."**[12]

Jacob worked for his uncle Laban for 20 years. During this time, he married Laban's two daughters, Leah and Rachel, along with their maids. God blessed everything Jacob did, despite his uncle's constant efforts to cheat him. As a result, he acquired great wealth.

How Israel Got Its Name

Laban's sons became jealous of Jacob because of God's blessings to him. So they turned their father's attitude against Jacob. Jacob still feared his brother Esau and hesitated to go back to Canaan. But the LORD said to Jacob, **"Return to the land of your fathers and to your relatives, and I will be with you."**[13]

---

12. Genesis 28:1–5 (NKJV).

13. Genesis 31:3.

Something mysterious happened to Jacob along the way. He sent his family by two companies ahead of him and he spent the night alone. Then a man appeared to him and wrestled with him all night. When he did not prevail against Jacob, he dislocated Jacob's leg at the hip. Then the man said to Jacob, **"Let me go, for the dawn is breaking."** But Jacob said to him, **"I will not let you go unless you bless me."**

Then the man said to Jacob, "What is your name?" And he replied, "Jacob" (which means, *the one who deceives*). At this point, an amazing thing is revealed. The man said to him, **"Your name will no longer be Jacob, but Israel,** (Israel means *he struggles with God*) **because you have struggled with God and with men and have overcome." Jacob said, "Please tell me your name." But he replied, "Why do you ask my name?" Then he blessed him there. So Jacob called the place Peniel,** (Peniel means *face of God*) **saying, "It is because I saw God face to face, and yet my life was spared."** [14]

There are enormous theological implications to this account. But simply put, the Second Person of the Godhead assumed the form of a man and condescended to wrestle with Jacob. Whenever God expresses Himself visibly or audibly, it is through the Second Person. This is the same one who later permanently joined Himself to a true human nature in the person of Jesus Christ.

When this incident was over, Jacob realized he had seen God face to face. He was in awe that God had graciously condescended to be intimately close to him and had not killed him.

From this time onward, Jacob's redeemed name was "Israel." After this, God often called him Jacob to emphasize his fleshly condition and Israel to emphasize his spiritual position. The same idea is expressed when God refers to the nation as either "the children of Jacob" or "the children of Israel".

---

14. Genesis 31:24–30.

The LORD reconfirms this new name when Jacob reached Bethel in Canaan. This is the place where God appeared to him long before when he first fled from Esau. Jacob built an altar there. It is at this time that the LORD gave Jacob one of His most important revelations:

> **Then God appeared to Jacob again when he came from Paddan-Aram, and He blessed him. And God said to him, "Your name is Jacob** [cheater]**; You shall no longer be called Jacob, But Israel shall be your name." Thus He called him Israel.**
>
> **God also said to him, "I am God Almighty; Be fruitful and multiply; A nation and a company of nations shall come from you, and kings shall come forth from you. And the land which I gave to Abraham and Isaac, I will give it to you, and I will give the land to your descendants after you."** [15]

Israel became the name of the chosen people of God. The name *Israel* appears in 1,695 verses of the Bible, both in the Old and New Testaments. This is very important because in their zeal to replace Israel, the Muslim's most serious charge against the Jews is that they corrupted the revelation God gave them.

Divine providence worked mightily concerning this name nearly 4000 years later. On the evening of May 14, 1948, David Ben Gurion and the original founders of the modern State of Israel still could not decide what they should call it. It was at the last moment that Ben Gurion said its name should be Israel. Thus unwittingly, prophecies concerning the nation in the later days were fulfilled—even to its name.

Birth of the Tribal States of Israel

A very essential part of this history is that Jacob had twelve sons to whom the covenants were confirmed. These sons were born

---

15. Genesis 35:9–12.

to him through his wives Leah and Rachel, and their two maids, Bilhah and Zilpah. As previously mentioned, the custom of that day was that if a man's wife was either barren or became barren, she could produce legal heirs by using her maid as a surrogate mother. In this case, Jacob married them all.

It is interesting to note that when Abraham followed this custom, it was not acceptable to God. But in this case God did accept it. Why?—It can only be understood in the light of God's purpose and sovereign grace. One thing is clear, in Abraham's case, the cause of using the maid to produce an heir was lack of faith in God's promise.

Leah gave birth to Reuben, the firstborn; then Simeon, Levi, Judah, Issachar, Zebulun and a daughter, Dinah.

Rachel's maid, Bilhah, gave birth to Dan and Naphtali.

Leah's maid, Zilpah, gave birth to Gad and Asher.

Rachel, who had been barren, finally gave birth to Joseph and the youngest son, Benjamin.

Altogether, Jacob had twelve sons who were accepted by God as the foundation of the tribal states of His chosen nation, which He would name Israel.

There was just one more addition to these tribal states. By an act of Divine providence, the two sons of Joseph who were born while he was in Egypt were given an inheritance and land among this original number. Their names were Ephraim and Manasseh. And because Levi committed a particularly heinous sin in God's eyes, his tribe was not given any land. But God graciously turned this curse into blessing when he made the Levites the priests of Israel. As it is written, **"Therefore Levi has no portion nor inheritance with his brethren; the Lord is his inheritance, just as the Lord your God promised him."** [16]

---

16. Deuteronomy 10:9 (NKJV).

Providence Saves the Nation

Joseph became the favorite son of his father, Jacob. As a result, Joseph's jealous brothers sold him into Egyptian slavery and told Jacob a wild animal had killed him. By the amazing work of Divine providence, Joseph rose from being a slave to becoming second in power to the mighty Pharaoh of Egypt.

Afterward, a famine gripped the entire world of the Mediterranean Sea. God warned Joseph that this was coming, so he prepared Egypt for the calamity. When the famine hit, Jacob and all his family were about to starve. So he sent ten of his sons to Egypt to buy grain. He only kept Benjamin, the youngest at home with him.

By God's providence, these brothers had to bargain for their lives with the very one they had maliciously sold into slavery. They did not recognize Joseph at first, but he knew them. He was now the mighty lord and co-regent of Egypt. When he finally revealed to them who he was, they were utterly terrified. They thought they were dead men.

But Joseph viewed the whole episode from the Divine viewpoint. He graciously forgave them and said:

> **"I am your brother Joseph, whom you sold into Egypt. And now do not be grieved or angry with yourselves, because you sold me here; for God sent me before you to preserve life. For the famine has been in the land these two years, and there are still five years in which there will be neither plowing nor harvesting. And God sent me before you to preserve for you a remnant in the earth, and to keep you alive by a great deliverance.**
>
> **"Now, therefore, it was not you who sent me here, but God; and He has made me a father to Pharaoh and lord of all his household and ruler over all the land of Egypt. "Hurry and go up to my father, and say to him, 'Thus says your son Joseph, "God has made me lord of all Egypt; come down to me, do not delay.**
>
> **"And you shall live in the land of Goshen, and you shall**

be near me, you and your children and your children's children and your flocks and your herds and all that you have. There I will also provide for you, for there are still five years of famine to come, lest you and your household and all that you have be impoverished.'" [17]

When Jacob's sons returned with a new invention of Egypt, wagons, and lavish provisions of food, Jacob could hardly believe it. And then when he was told that Joseph was alive and now the lord of Egypt, he was overwhelmed. When Jacob finally believed, God appeared to him and explained His purpose in it all:

And God spoke to Israel in visions of the night and said, "Jacob, Jacob." And he said, "Here I am." And He said, "I am God, the God of your father; do not be afraid to go down to Egypt, for I will make you a great nation there. I will go down with you to Egypt, and I will also surely bring you up (to the Promised Land) **again; and Joseph will close your eyes."** [18]

This began the fulfillment of the prophecy to Abraham, mentioned earlier, concerning the period of 400 years in which his descendants would grow into a nation in a land that was not their own.[19] And even though they would later be made slaves, God promised He would judge that nation and cause them to come out with great wealth.

As for Joseph, his life perfectly illustrated the power of a promise made in the New Testament. **"And we know that God causes all things to work together for good to those who love God, to those who are called according to His purpose."** [20] Joseph assessed his whole experience from the Divine viewpoint; **"But Joseph said to them** (his brothers), **'Do not be afraid, for am I in God's place? And as for you, you meant evil against me, but God**

---

17. Genesis 45:4–11.

18. Genesis 46:2–4.

19. Genesis 15:13–16 (NIV).

20. Romans 8:28.

meant it for good in order to bring about this present result, to preserve many people alive.'" [21]

All things are not good. But when we trust the LORD with our problems, He works even the bad things together for good. And in the process He gives us peace of mind and rest in the midst of trouble. This is the secret to a long life.

Joseph's Experiences Preview the Messiah's

For centuries, both Jews and Christians have recognized the parallel between Joseph's experiences and those of the Messiah.

Of course, the Israelites have not fully recognized the identity of the One this symbolizes, but some rabbis who lived before Jesus was born did theorize that there must be two Messiahs that are to come. They recognized that there are two difference portraits of the Messiah painted in Bible prophecy. One is a conquering King who will come in great power and glory to deliver Israel from a great holocaust and set them up in the kingdom promised to their fathers. This Messiah they called the Son of David.

The other portrait predicts the Messiah will come as a lowly servant who will suffer for the transgressions of his people. This Messiah they call the Son of Joseph because of the obvious parallels.

What is not yet recognized by Israel is that there is only one Messiah who comes at two different times. The first time he comes as the Suffering Servant, and the second as the Conquering King of David's seed.

Just look at the parallel between Joseph and Jesus.

- Joseph was rejected by his brothers and sent to die at the hands of the Gentiles.

---

21. Genesis 50:19–20 (NKJV).

- Jesus was also rejected and turned over to the Gentiles for crucifixion.

- Joseph was received and given great honor and glory among the Gentiles.
- Jesus also has been received and honored among the Gentiles.

- While among the Gentiles, Joseph had children that were later included in the covenant blessings of Abraham, Isaac and Joseph.
- Jesus has also been given children among the Gentiles who have been adopted into the covenants of Israel.

- When great calamity came upon the world, the only salvation for Joseph's brothers was through the very one they had rejected. He who was thought to be dead "came back to life" and saved them.
- In the same way, Bible prophecy predicts that a tribulation will sweep the whole world and only Jesus will save Israel when they turn to Him:

  > **And I will pour out on the house of David and the inhabitants of Jerusalem the Spirit of grace and supplication. They will look on me, the one they have pierced, and they will mourn for him as one mourns for an only child, and grieve bitterly for him as one grieves for a firstborn son.** [22]

- When Joseph's brothers came seeking help and later acknowledged their sin, Joseph forgave and saved them and settled them in his kingdom.
- When Jesus' brothers, the Israelites, finally acknowledge their sin and seek Him, He is going to save them and settle them in His promised kingdom.

---

22. Zechariah 12:10 (NIV).

Genesis Finalizes Who Are God's Chosen People

The Book of Genesis gives the complete record as to who God's chosen people are through Abraham. Now stop and think about this for a moment. The Bible teaches as much by the amount of space given to a subject as it does by what it says.

God took only eleven chapters to record the account of mankind from his creation until the call of Abraham. This covers perhaps thousands of years. But God took from chapter twelve to chapter fifty—a period of about 300 years—to cover the creation and establishment of His chosen people. To those who believe the Bible, this should speak volumes about the importance God places upon them.

Genesis ends with a careful accounting of the descendants of Abraham, Isaac, Jacob, Jacob's sons and all their families as they go into Egypt.

The fact that the Bible repeatedly records genealogies is boring to most people. Almost all of these are records of the children of Abraham, Isaac and Jacob. The important question is, Why are there so many? Why such a careful record of these people—particularly if they are to be ultimately rejected and abandoned as the Preterists group believes?

And more to the issue of our day, the Muslims believe that the Israelites never were God's chosen people. They believe that Ishmael and his Arab descendants got cheated out of their proper inheritance, since he was Abraham's firstborn son. As we will see, today's Muslim doctrine is that "the people of the Book"[23] falsified the original revelation and made themselves the heirs of God's covenants.

---

23. Muslims teach that the Israelites were entrusted with God's written revelation, but that they so changed and distorted its original message that Allah sent Mohammad to recover "the Truth", which he received in the Koran.

The Biblical Record

The verse I quoted at the beginning of this chapter sets the record straight. God spoke this to Moses from out of the burning bush when he called him to lead the Israelites out of Egypt:

> **Say to the Israelites, "The LORD, the God of your fathers —the God of Abraham, the God of Isaac and the God of Jacob—has sent me to you." This is my name forever, the name by which I am to be remembered from generation to generation.**[24]

This name is confirmed throughout the rest of the Bible. But most importantly, the Lord Jesus Christ Himself confirms it:

> **But about the resurrection of the dead—have you not read what God said to you, "I AM the God of Abraham, the God of Isaac, and the God of Jacob." He is not the God of the dead but of the living.**[25]

When Jesus corrected the Jewish Sadducee sect's denial of the resurrection, He quoted God's statement to Moses, emphasizing what God said to them. His whole argument is based on the Hebrew verbal construction for "being", illustrating that God *continuously* is the God of Abraham, Isaac and Jacob. Therefore, they must be living, since God doesn't have a relationship with the dead. Also, inherent in this statement is that God will always be in a covenant relationship with them and their descendants.

This name, Yahweh or Jehovah [I Am], cannot apply to the Church—not even in a figurative sense. It is also a name that cannot be applied to the Muslims.

Why is this so important? We will see that the God of the Bible is not the God of Ishmael, Esau, Mohammad and the Muslims. Indeed we will see that this issue is not just some irrelevant old theological argument, but is one of the central issues that is about to drag the whole world into war.

---

23. Exodus 3:15 (NIV).
24. Matthew 22:31–32 (NIV).

CHAPTER FOUR

Abraham's Wild Child:
The Hate Begins

*He will be a wild ass of a man; his hand will be
against everyone and everyone's hand against him,
and he will live in hostility toward all his brothers
and dwell to the east of them.*

GOD'S PROPHECY ABOUT ISHMAEL
GENESIS 16:12 (NIV)

S ome decisions we make in life carry consequences far beyond our comprehension. There are some things we would give anything to undo, but alas, they cannot be. What is worse, there are some sins that are generational, that is, the consequences of our wrong choices can extend to our relatives for generations.

Abraham had a lapse of faith concerning God's promise to give him a son. The decision he made during this episode of unbelief resulted in such enormous consequences that they have continued through the centuries until this very hour. I am sure that if Abraham had even a small hint of the trouble that would follow, he would never have tried to help God give him a son.

This is the account of how a temporary lapse of faith resulted in catastrophe for Abraham's future descendants who inherited the covenants. The consequences have effected about a hundred generations over a period of 4000 years.

Some of the history in this chapter will overlap with that of the last. But since this history is so critical to the understanding of the modern Arab-Israeli conflict, it is necessary. This chapter will emphasize Ishmael's role in this 4000-year-old family feud.

Abraham's Lapse of Faith

Abraham turned 85. It had been ten years since he moved to Canaan and God made the covenants with him that guaranteed He would give him a son. And Sarah, his wife, was becoming very impatient. Finally, she decided that since she was 75 and still barren, it was impossible for her to bear Abraham a son. So Sarah came up with the following plan:

Now Sarai, Abram's wife, had borne him no children. But she had an Egyptian maidservant named Hagar; so she said to Abram, "The LORD has kept me from having children. Go, sleep with my maidservant; perhaps I can build a family through her." Abram agreed to what Sarai said. So after Abram had been living in Canaan ten years, Sarai his wife took her Egyptian maidservant

Hagar and gave her to her husband to be his wife. He slept with Hagar, and she conceived. When she knew she was pregnant, she began to despise her mistress.[2]

Sarah decided that the LORD had prevented her from conceiving and decided He must have another plan for giving them an heir. She assumed that the LORD needed some help. The custom for the world of that time, as I mentioned before, was for the wife to use her maid as a surrogate mother. So Abraham, whose own faith must have been wavering, agreed with Sarah's plan.

The big problem with this plan was that it grew from unbelief in God's promise. Sarah and Abraham looked at this problem from the human viewpoint (HVP). The human viewpoint sees a problem from the standpoint of human ability. On the other hand, the divine viewpoint (DVP) looks at a problem from the standpoint of God's ability to solve it.

So Abraham, at the suggestion of his wife, had relations with the Egyptian maid. And the moment she conceived, the problems began. The maid's attitude changed and a civil war developed in the tents of Abraham.

This situation was predictable. Proverbs warns:

Under three things the earth trembles, under four it cannot bear up: a servant who becomes king, a fool who is full of food, an unloved woman who is married, and *a maidservant who displaces her mistress.*[3]

To make matters even worse, Sarah blamed Abraham for following her idea. Sarai said to Abram,

"You are responsible for the wrong I am suffering. I put my servant in your arms, and now that she knows she is pregnant, she despises me. May the LORD judge between you and me."[4]

---

2. Genesis 16:1–4 (NIV).

3. Proverbs 30:21–23 (NIV), emphasis added.

4. Genesis 16:5 (NIV).

Abraham uncharacteristically evaded the problem and threw it back into Sarah's lap. He told her, "She's your maid, you deal with her. Do whatever you want with her." And, of course, Sarah vented her frustration and anger on poor Hagar. She treated her so harshly that Hagar ran away into the desert.

God's Prophecy to Hagar

No doubt Hagar would have died in the desert had not the LORD in His great mercy sought her out and encouraged her. The angel of the LORD[5] gave Hagar a great promise and a prophecy about the child she would bear:

> **The angel of the LORD found Hagar near a spring in the desert; it was the spring that is beside the road to Shur. And he said, "Hagar, servant of Sarai, where have you come from, and where are you going?" "I'm running away from my mistress Sarai," she answered.**
>
> **Then the angel of the LORD told her, "Go back to your mistress and submit to her." The angel added, "I will so increase your descendants that they will be too numerous to count." The angel of the LORD also said to her: "You are now with child and you will have a son. You shall name him Ishmael,** (Ishmael means God hears) **for the LORD has heard of your misery.**
>
> **"He will be a wild ass of a man; his hand will be against everyone and everyone's hand against him, and he will live in hostility toward all his brothers [and he shall dwell to the east them]."[6]**

This was a marvelous manifestation of the mercy of God. She apparently was trying to follow the road across the Sinai back to

---

5. Orthodox theologians agree that the Angel of the LORD, who appeared all through the Old Testament and ceased after the birth of Jesus, was the pre-incarnate Messiah Jesus, the Second Person of the Godhead. No doubt this is the phenomenon to which Jesus was referring when He said, "Your father Abraham rejoiced to see My day, and he saw it and was glad." Then the Jews said to Him, "You are not yet fifty years old, and have You seen Abraham?" Jesus said to them, "Most assuredly, I say to you, before Abraham was, I AM." (John 8:56–58).

6. Genesis 16:7–12 (NIV).

Egypt. But most likely, she would have died in route. Hagar, the Egyptian maid, was involved in an affair over which she had no choice. But the **LORD** demonstrated that He loved her too, as He does anyone who calls out to Him and throws himself upon God's mercy. The very name that God gives her for the son she carried is a memorial that the LORD heard her prayer of distress. He commanded her to name him Ish-ma-el, which means *God hears*.

A lone runaway female slave in that day was truly helpless and in danger. The LORD therefore told her to return and be submissive to Sarah with the promise that He would bless her with descendents through her son that would be beyond numbering. She is promised her own inheritance and blessing from the LORD through her son.

Because Ishmael is also a son of Abraham, God promised to bless him and make him into a great multitude of people and nations. The LORD then made one of His amazing prophecies about the kind of temperament and nature that would be in Ishmael's genes, and then passed on to his descendents. It is fascinating to analyze each clause and to see how accurately it has been fulfilled in the descendents of Ishmael—the Arabs.

'HE WILL BE A WILD ASS OF A MAN . . .'

Hebrew scholars Keil and Delitzsch write about how accurately this metaphor describes the Arab:

> "The figure of a wild ass, that wild and untamable animal, roaming at its will in the desert . . . depicts most aptly the Bedouin's boundless love of freedom as he rides about in the desert, spear in hand, upon his camel or his horse, hardy, frugal, reveling in the varied beauty of nature, and despising town life in every form."[7]

---

7. Keil, C. F., and Delitzsch, F. "Genesis", in vol. 1: *The Pentateuch*. Translated by James Martin, *Commentary on the Old Testament*. 10 vols. N.p.; reprint ed., (Grand Rapids, MI.: William B. Eerdmans Publishing Co., 1983), p. 220.

God poetically describes the nature of the wild ass in His challenge to Job:

> **Who set the wild ass free?**
> **Who loosed the bonds of the swift ass,**
> **Whose home I have made the wilderness,**
> **And the barren land his dwelling?**
> **He scorns the tumult of the city;**
> **He does not heed the shouts of the driver.**
> **The range of the mountains is his pasture,**
> **And he searches after every green thing.**[8]

This perfectly describes the nature and genetic characteristics of Ishmael and his descendants, the Arabs. Like the donkeys of the wilderness, they fiercely love their freedom and independence. They have always had a warrior's temperament.

'WHOSE HOME I HAVE MADE THE WILDERNESS, AND THE BARREN LAND HIS DWELLING . . .'

God predicted that the Ishmaelites would live to the east of all his brethren. God gave them the Arabian Peninsula, which is to the east of all the rest of Abraham's descendants. It is the largest Peninsula in the world. Philip Hitti writes about the Arab home:

> Despite its size—it is the largest peninsula in the world—its total population is estimated at only seven to eight million. It is one of the driest and hottest countries in the whole world. True, the area is sandwiched between seas on the east and west, but these bodies of water are too narrow to break the climactic continuity of the Africo-Asian rainless continental masses. The ocean on the south does bring rains, to be sure, but the monsoons (an Arabic word, incidentally), which seasonally lash the land, leave very little moisture for the interior. It is easy to understand why the bracing and delightful east wind has always provided a favorite theme for Arabian poets.[9]

---

8. Job 39:5–8 (from Hebrew text)

9. Philip K. Hitti, *The Arabs: A Short History*, (Washington DC: Regnery Publishing, Inc., 1996), <http://www.oneworldmagazine.org/focus/deserts/toc.htm>.

The migrant Arab is called a "Bedouin". He loves the desert and the freedom to move with the seasons about the vast barren regions from oasis to oasis—*always searching after every green thing.*

The Arabs call their Peninsula an "Island" because it is surrounded on three sides by ocean—and to the north where it connects to land, the great Nafud Desert isolates it.

The richest part of Arabia in ancient history was the southern coast, which thrust out into the Indian Ocean and rounded to the Red Sea. This area received seasonal rains and produced some of the most exotic and valuable plants of the ancient world. The much sought after fragrance called myrrh came from there. Arabia also accumulated great wealth because its seaports were along the main trade route from Asia.

'HIS HAND WILL BE AGAINST EVERYONE AND EVERYONE'S HAND WILL BE AGAINST HIM . . .'

This characteristic has been dominant throughout the history of the Arabs. Hitti summarizes accurately the Arab Bedouin nature:

> The Bedouin still lives, as his forebears did, in tents of goats' or camels' hair ("houses of hair"), and grazes his sheep and goats on the same ancient pastures. Sheep-and-camel-raising, and to a lesser degree horse-breeding, *hunting and raiding,* are his regular occupations, and are to his mind the only occupations worthy of a man.[10]

Blood feuds have been fought between the many Arab tribes of the Peninsula for centuries. Their lists of grudges against each other are ancient. If an Arab is forced out of the protection of his tribe, he usually doesn't last very long.

The wild donkey reflects this very characteristic. He groups together in small herds and is hostile with even other herds of his own kind. Similarly Arab society from its earliest history divided

---

10. Ibid., emphasis added.

up into many clans. Again, Hitti describes the predominant Arab social structure:

> The spirit of the clan demands boundless and uncondi-tional loyalty to fellow clansmen, a passionate chauvinism. His allegiance, which is individualism of the member mag-nified, assumes that his tribe is a unit by itself, self-suffi-cient and absolute, *and regards every other tribe as its legitimate victim and object of plunder and murder.*[11]

There have been only a few things able to unite Arabs in all their history. The most important unifier was Mohammad and the initial impact of the Muslim religion. But over time, even religion could not hold the different Arab tribes together.

Then there was the common threat to their "Holy Places" posed by the Catholic Crusaders. Muslim armies united to fight off the successive waves of European knights sent by the Pope to lib-erate Jerusalem and ancient Israel.

In our present era, the most powerful unifying factor of all has arisen. Nothing can unite the warring Muslim factions like their age-old hatred for Jews and the reborn State of Israel. To the Muslims, the State of Israel's existence in the midst of what they consider their sacred sphere of the world is the ultimate sacrilege. It is an insult to Allah that must be avenged. To the Muslim, the fact that Israel has beaten them in five wars threatens the veraci-ty of the Koran, which promises them victory over the infidels, especially when it is a "Jihad to liberate their third holiest site— Jerusalem." This is a "humiliation" that must be avenged for the sake and honor of Allah and the sacred Koran. This escalates to a level of religious passion that cannot be fathomed by the West.

Much more will be said on this subject later in the book.

---

11. Ibid., emphasis added.

'. . . AND HE WILL LIVE IN HOSTILITY TOWARD ALL OF HIS BROTHERS, [AND HE WILL DWELL TO THE EAST OF THEM.]'

This part of the prophecy concerning Ishmael and his descendants is particularly important. Many English translations simply translate this clause as, ". . . and he will dwell to the east of all his brothers." But the Hebrew words and grammatical construction are much more complex than that translation would imply.

Keil and Delitzsch observe,

"He will dwell before the face of all his brethren." עַל פְּנֵי denotes, it is true, to the east of (cf. chap. xxv. 18), and this meaning is also to be retained here; but the geographical notice of the dwelling place of the Ishmaelites hardly exhausts the force of the expression, which also indicated that Ishmael would maintain an independent standing before (in the presence of) all the descendants of Abraham. History has confirmed this promise. The Ishmaelites have continued to this day in free and undiminished possession of the extensive peninsula between the Euphrates, the Straits of Suez, and the Red Sea, from which they have overspread both Northern Africa and Southern Asia."[12]

The Hebrew expression *in the face of* can also mean, *to stand in defiant hostility toward.* I believe the New International Version correctly expresses the sense of it, **". . . and he will live in hostility toward all his brothers."** So does the New Revised Standard Version, **". . . and he shall live at odds with all his kin."** However, it is my opinion that the NIV translation better catches the intended meaning. History has also confirmed this to be the more accurate translation.

---

12. Keil and Delitzsch, *The Pentateuch*, pp. 220–221.

Enmity Flashes in Embryonic Form

The seeds of enmity are expressed in embryonic form on the occasion of the Isaac's weaning. Abraham and Sarah threw a great feast to celebrate. By this time, Ishmael was at least 16 years old and accustomed to having most of his father's attention. So when Isaac was born and so much attention was showered upon him, a great deal of resentment and jealousy must have sprung up in both Ishmael and his mother. All the ingredients for a civil war in the tents of Abraham were present.

During the celebration, the Bible reports, **"And Sarah saw the son of Hagar the Egyptian, whom she had borne to Abraham, scoffing** [at her son Isaac]."[13]

Scoffing is translated from the Hebrew root word "to laugh" (צהק). But in the participial form of this context it means *making fun of, ridiculing, discounting someone's worth.*

To understand the full implications of this situation, we have to put it up against the background of the promise God gave to Abraham when He announced Isaac's birth. God had promised Abraham:

> **Then God said to Abraham, "As for Sarai your wife, you shall not call her name Sarai, but Sarah shall be her name. And I will bless her and also give you a son by her; then I will bless her, and she shall be a mother of nations; kings of peoples shall be from her." Then Abraham fell on his face and laughed, and said in his heart, "Shall a child be born to a man who is one hundred years old? And shall Sarah, who is ninety years old, bear a child?" And Abraham said to God, "Oh, that Ishmael might live before You!" Then God said: "No, Sarah your wife shall bear you a son, and you shall call his name Isaac; I will establish My covenant with him for an everlasting covenant, and with his descendants after him."[14]**

---

13. Genesis 21:9 (NKJV)
14. Genesis 17:15–19 (NKJV).

This God given revelation was certainly made known to Abraham's entire household, including Hagar and Ishmael. And its Divine authenticity was confirmed with the miraculous conception and birth of Isaac to his elderly parents.

So when Ishmael scoffed at and made fun of Isaac, he did so with the knowledge that according to Divine revelation, Isaac was the chosen one. And that was not merely a human choice based on carnal favoritism. This is why in the eyes of God Ishmael was not just mocking Isaac, but he was rejecting and ridiculing His sovereign choice. The German scholar Hengstenberg expressed the following insight, "Unbelief, envy, pride of carnal superiority, were the causes of Ishmael's conduct . . ."[15]

This is the stuff of which enmity was born in Ishmael. Remember, *enmity* is hatred that has been nourished over a long period of time. It was now just beginning to take root.

God's Promises to Ishmael

The Bible makes it clear that despite the birth of Isaac, there was no lack of love for Ishmael on the part of Abraham or God. Abraham even petitioned the Lord that Ishmael could be part of the Divine choice when he said, **"Oh, that Ishmael might live before You!"**

As a result, God made it clear that Ishmael would be given a great inheritance because he was also Abraham's son. God promised:

> **"And as for Ishmael, I have heard you. Behold, I have blessed him, and will make him fruitful, and will multiply him exceedingly. He shall beget twelve princes, and I will make him a great nation. But My covenant I will establish with Isaac, whom Sarah shall bear to you at this set time next year."[16]**

---

15. Keil and Delitzsch, *The Pentateuch*, quoted on p. 244.
16. Genesis 17:20–21 (NKJV).

In point of fact, the Ishmaelites were given more land and ultimately more wealth than Israelites. This was true in their past history, not to mention the vast oil wealth of modern times. And Spiritual salvation has always been open to the Ishmaelites.

But God's covenant, which concerned His spiritual purposes, was only for Isaac and his descendants. The physical blessings promised to Isaac were to facilitate God's spiritual call for the nation that would come from him.

Why God Separated Ishmael and Isaac

What happened as a result of Ishmael's actions might seem too severe unless it is seen in the light of the Divine perspective. When Sarah saw how Ishmael scoffed at her son, she said to Abraham (I'm sure without altogether spiritual motives), **"Get rid of that slave woman and her son, for that slave woman's son will never share in the inheritance with my son Isaac."** [17]

This really grieved Abraham. But in this case, God saw the spiritual necessity of separating the two. Perhaps if Ishmael had not yielded to the fleshly passions of envy and jealousy, he and his mother could have stayed with the family. But this episode showed that he was not looking at this from the standpoint of God's sovereign purpose and choice. He was only focusing on the situation from his carnal human emotions that said, "What God gave me is not enough—I want it all." And as we will see, the Ishmaelites are still saying, "What God gave us is not enough, we want it all". Now this feeling is driven by centuries of enmity.

Ishmael's wrong attitude is certainly a common human failure. How often I have seen even Christian ministers become ungrateful for the spiritual gifts and blessings God has given them when they become jealous of the gifts God gave others. That's always a very costly yielding to the old sin nature. The Scriptures say, **"But one and the same Spirit works all these things, distributing [spir-**

---

17. Genesis 21:10 (NIV).

itual gifts] to each one individually as He wills." [18] So the greatly grieved Abraham gave Hagar her freedom and provisions for her and Ishmael and sent them away. I am sure it took real faith on Abraham's part to trust that God would take care of them—because he did love Ishmael.

"God Hears" Ishmael

When the provisions and water ran out, which I am sure was designed to be God's test of their faith, they despaired. Remember, the meaning of Ishmael's name is *God Hears*. Ishmael cried out to God, and the LORD graciously heard his cry,

> **God heard the boy crying, and the angel of God called to Hagar from heaven and said to her, "What is the matter, Hagar? Do not be afraid; God has heard the boy crying as he lies there. Lift the boy up and take him by the hand, for I will make him into a great nation." Then God opened her eyes and she saw a well of water. So she went and filled the skin with water and gave the boy a drink.** [19]

Hagar and Ishmael were given great privileges. This is the second time that The LORD appeared to Hagar, spoke with her and rescued her. This was also a gracious revelation to Ishmael. If these two did not receive God's redemption, it could never be said they had no light. How many today could truly say that God appeared and spoke with them?

The LORD never abandoned Ishmael. The Bible records, **"God was with the boy as he grew up. He lived in the desert and became an archer. While he was living in the Desert of Paran, his mother got a wife for him from Egypt."** [20]

Ishmael is not mentioned again until the death of his father Abraham. Then Isaac and Ishmael came together and buried their

---

18. 1 Corinthians 12:11.
19. Genesis 21:17–19 (NIV).

father. Apparently they then went their separate ways and did not see each other again.

Ishmael's Legacy

Ishmael had twelve sons, each of whom became a great prince and founded a nation. However, the second son, Kedar, became the most powerful and wealthy. Remember that name, for his descendants figure prominently in Arab history.

God blessed Ishmael and caused him to live 137 years. This is God's obituary for him:

> **Altogether, Ishmael lived a hundred and thirty-seven years. He breathed his last and died, and he was gathered to his people. His descendants settled in the area from Havilah to Shur, near the border of Egypt, as you go toward Asshur. *And they lived in hostility toward all their brothers.*** [21]

Amazing! Exactly the same thing said about Ishmael's descendants was said of him. It is exactly the same Hebrew clause, except instead of "he", it is "they" who continued to live in "hostility toward all their brothers" and "dwelt to the east of them". And of course the brothers, against whom this hostility is directed, are the descendants of Isaac who lived to the west.

How that hostility became enmity is the focus of the rest of this book. Read on, for you also will be directly affected by this ancient family feud.

---

20. Genesis 21:20–21 (NIV).
21. Genesis 25:17–18 (NIV).

CHAPTER FIVE

'Cursed' Be the Tie that Binds

*Now Abraham gave all that he had to Isaac; but to the **sons of his concubines**, Abraham gave gifts while he was still living, and sent them away from his son Isaac **eastward, to the land of the east.***

GENESIS 25:5, EMPHASIS ADDED

So Esau hated Jacob because of the blessing with which his father blessed him, and Esau said in his heart, "The days of mourning for my father are at hand; then I will kill my brother Jacob."

GENESIS 27:41

Never in history has there been a family feud that sustained such enmity over so long a period of time. And no other ethnic violence has ever affected so many nations as this one is about to do. Indeed, the Bible predicts that the last war of the world will be triggered by a conflict between the descendants of these ancient family members.

This is why it is so important to trace these peoples through history to the present day. And it is of ultimate importance to understand the root cause of the common hatred they have all embraced toward Israel.

I believe this is the biggest single factor misunderstood by today's Western diplomats and media. And it is the reason all of their attempts to solve the Middle East conflict are destined for failure.

To my knowledge, no one has done extensive research on the Abraham's family history and the source of the tremendous enmity against his descendants through Isaac. So, follow closely in this section. It will throw some very important light on today's Middle East problems.

The Curse of Abraham's Nephew

When God called Abraham, He told him very specifically to **"Get out of your country, from your kindred, and from your father's house, to a land that I will show you."** [1] Now the record shows that Abraham (then called Abram) only *partially obeyed* the LORD's command. For when he left Ur of the Chaldeans, his father, Terah, was in charge and went with him as far as Haran, which was only part of the way to Canaan. It appears that the LORD did not allow Abraham to even enter Canaan until after his father died in Haran. [2] God wanted Abraham to be in charge of his own household. Ancient tradition has always established the

---

1. Genesis 12:1 (NKJV).
2. See Genesis 11:27–32.

eldest male as the chief of the family.

After Abraham's father died, we read:

> So Abram departed as the LORD had spoken to him, and Lot went with him. And Abram was seventy-five years old when he departed from Haran. Then Abram took Sarai his wife and Lot his brother's son, and all their possessions that they had gathered, and the people whom they had acquired in Haran, and they departed to go to the land of Canaan. So they came to the land of Canaan. Abram passed through the land to the place of Shechem, as far as the terebinth tree of Moreh. And the Canaanites were then in the land. Then the LORD appeared to Abram and said, "To your descendants I will give this land." And there he built an altar to the LORD, who had appeared to him. [3]

Even though Abraham was now in charge of the family, he still did not fully obey the LORD, for he took Lot, his nephew, with him. And Lot became the proverbial albatross around his neck.

Later, when Abraham and Lot tried to live together, a range war developed between their two groups of "cowboys" and shepherds. Both had too many livestock to survive in the same region.

Lot's Carnal Choice

So Abraham, the senior, graciously allowed Lot first choice as to where in the land he would like to settle. Lot's choice was purely of the flesh. He chose the lush plain of the Jordan River. Here is the Bible's description:

> And Lot lifted his eyes and saw all the plain of Jordan, that it was well watered everywhere (before the Lord destroyed Sodom and Gomorrah) like the garden of the LORD, like the land of Egypt as you go toward Zoar. Then Lot chose for himself all the plain of Jordan, and Lot journeyed east. And they separated from each other.

---

3. Genesis 12:4–7 NKJ.

Abram dwelt in the land of Canaan, and Lot dwelt in the cities of the plain and pitched his tent even as far as Sodom. But the men of Sodom were exceedingly wicked and sinful against the LORD.

Many interesting facts are revealed here. The area that is now the Dead Sea was like the Garden of Eden before God's overwhelming judgment upon the cities of Sodom and Gomorrah. The tremendous explosion that hit these two cities must have landed like a giant karate chop, as this area is now a rift valley. The center, where Sodom and Gomorrah were, is like a moveable stage that is between two parallel fault lines extending from Mount Hermon in the north to Lake Tanganyika in Africa to the south. This region is 1,260 feet below sea level.

Standing atop Masada, I have seen some of the ruins of Sodom under the southern tip of the Dead Sea. Anyone who doubts God's attitude toward sodomy only needs to look at this geographical reminder.

Lot's Downward Path

The Bible records that Lot first pitched his tent toward Sodom. It is later revealed that he moved into the city of Sodom and settled there. Then his troubles really began. It was apparently the influence of his wife that drove him from tents into the luxury of the city, but they paid a terrible price, as revealed in Genesis 19. The people of the city were consumed with every form of sexual perversion mixed with extreme violence.

When God revealed to Abraham that He was going to destroy Sodom and Gomorrah, he interceded for the wicked cities to save Lot and his family. God granted Abraham's desire, but not his petition. He delivered Lot and his family, but destroyed the wicked cities.

God's Grace Never Fails

Lot is held up as an example of God's unfailing grace to the carnal, believer:

> **. . . and [God] turning the cities of Sodom and Gomorrah into ashes, condemned them to destruction, making them an example to those who afterward would live ungodly; and delivered righteous Lot, who was oppressed by the filthy conduct of the wicked (for that righteous man, dwelling among them, tormented his righteous soul from day to day by seeing and hearing their lawless deeds)—then the Lord knows how to deliver the godly out of temptations and to reserve the unjust under punishment for the day of judgment . . .**[4]

Lot was out of fellowship and his conduct was not righteous, but his spirit was still born again and he had the righteousness of faith that comes with receiving God's pardon for sin. Though God disciplined him, He did not disown him.

Lot's Curse: Moab and Ammon

Now it was after this destruction and the death of Lot's wife (who turned back in her heart for the fleshly comforts of Sodom), that Lot became the father of two of Israel's greatest enemies.

Lot's two daughters feared since they were the only survivors of the entire region of Sodom and Gomorrah, they would never have husbands or offspring. In those days, children were like having social security for your old age.

So, each girl in turn made their father drunk and had sex with him. The result of this incest was the birth of two sons, Moab and Ammon. We will see that their descendants became the constant enemies of Israel. They are predicted to be part of an alliance of hate that is involved in the war that ends this present world order.

---

4. 2 Peter 2:6–9 (NKJV).

Abraham's Other Sons

A little considered part of Abraham's life is what happened to him after the death of Sarah, his wife. When she died, Abraham was 137-years-old. After Abraham provided Rebekah as a wife for Isaac, making sure the covenant line was settled, he married another wife. He was about 139 by this time.

We all marvel, and rightly so, that God enabled Abraham, against nature, to have Isaac at the age of 100 years. But here we find how far back God turned his biological clock and restored his youth. Here is the amazing and important record:

Abraham again took a wife, and her name was Keturah. And she bore him Zimran, Jokshan, Medan, Midian, Ishbak, and Shuah. Jokshan begot Sheba and Dedan. And the sons of Dedan were Asshurim, Letushim, and Leummim. And the sons of Midian were Ephah, Epher, Hanoch, Abidah, and Eldaah. All these were the children of Keturah.[5]

Abraham had six more sons and ten grandsons before his death at the age of 175 years. These are the people to whom the prophet Jeremiah refers in a prophetic warning to the nations that mistreated Israel. He refers to them as a part of the Arabian people, **"all the kings of Arabia and all the kings of the mixed multitude who dwell in the desert . . ."**[6]

The *mixed multitude* is no doubt descended from Abraham's other sons, who apparently mingled with the Ishmaelites in the vast Arabian Peninsula. This is supported by the Bible. Before Abraham died, the Word of God points out that he gave all he had to Isaac. Then it specifically notes, **"But Abraham gave gifts to the sons of the concubines which Abraham had; and while he was still living he sent them eastward, away from Isaac his son, to the country of the east."**[7]

5. Genesis 25:1–4 (NKJV).
6. Jeremiah 25:24 (NKV)J.
7. Genesis 25:6 (NKJV).

Note that it says "concubines" plural. Abraham only had two concubines—Ishmael's Egyptian mother Hagar and Keturah. So this would indicate he called them all together and gave gifts to Ishmael and the six sons he had with Keturah. Then he sent *them* (which in context would have to mean both Ishmael and his other six sons) *eastward, away from Isaac his son, to the country of the east.* The country to the east was the land that became known as the Arabian Peninsula.

The Perpetual Family Tie

I am sure the reason Abraham sent these family members to the east was to protect Isaac and his family. There was resentment and jealousy among the sons toward Isaac. They saw only the father's favoritism, not God's sovereign purpose.

This is the common factor that runs through all of Israel's relatives. *It is this enmity that developed from envy and jealousy which binds all of these family members together.*

Esau I Have Hated . . .

There are two descendants of Abraham that have been the most persistent enemies of Israel—Ishmael and Esau. As we have seen, Ishmael is the half brother of Isaac and Esau is the twin brother of Jacob. Much was observed about Esau in chapter three, but there are other factors that need to be noted here.

Esau and Jacob were fraternal twins. Fraternal twins are not only different in appearance, but usually very different in temperament and personality. This was glaringly so in the case of these two boys.

I have fraternal twin daughters that don't even look like sisters. Their temperaments and personalities are radically different. They represent two entirely different strains of their family's genes. But thank God, they are not like these two boys—they have always loved each other.

Esau, Who Is Called Edom

As mentioned in an earlier chapter, Esau was nicknamed "Edom" or "Red" apparently for two reasons. First, because from birth his body was covered with red hair. And second, because he called the lentil stew for which he sold his birth right, "that *red* stuff".

When Esau discovered that Jacob had tricked his father Isaac into giving him the blessing of the first born, which Esau had traded to Jacob for "red" lentil stew, he wept and begged for the oath to be reversed. But Isaac realized that what he had sworn before the Lord could not be undone. Instead, God made a prophecy through Isaac about Esau's future:

> **And he [Isaac] said, "Your brother came deceitfully, and has taken away your blessing." Then he [Esau] said, "Is he not rightly named Jacob, for he has *cheated*[8] me these two times? He took away my birthright, and behold, now he has taken away my blessing." And he said, "Have you not reserved a blessing for me?" But Isaac answered and said to Esau, "Behold, I have made him your master, and all his relatives I have given to him as servants; and with grain and new wine I have sustained him. Now as for you then, what can I do, my son?" And Esau said to his father, "Do you have only one blessing, my father? Bless me, even me also, O my father." So Esau lifted his voice and wept. Then Isaac his father answered and said to him, "Behold, away from the fertility of the earth shall be your dwelling, And away from the dew of heaven from above. And by your sword you shall live, and your brother you shall serve; But it shall come about when you become restless, that you shall break his yoke from your neck.[9]**

The Lord caused Isaac to unwillingly pronounce a sad future for his favorite son. The land where his descendants settled was

---

8. The Hebrew word for Jacob is usually translated "he who supplants." But today it is best understood as "he who cheats by deception" or simply "Cheater".

9. Genesis 27:35–40 (NKJV), emphasis added.

not fertile—it was primarily the Arabian Peninsula. They first set-tled in the mountains east of the Dead Sea that extended from its lower tip southward. But eventually, almost all of them migrated and mingled with the Ishmaelites, or Arabs.

By Your Sword You Shall Live

Like his uncle Ishmael, Esau would live by the sword. He would war and pillage to sustain his people. Keil and Delitzsch observe:

> **"Behold, away from the fertility of the earth shall be your dwelling, and away from the dew of heaven from above."** This is generally the condition of the mountainous coun-try of Edom, which although not without its fertile slopes and valleys, especially in the eastern portion, is thorough-ly waste and barren in the western; so that Seetzen says it consists of "the most desolate and barren mountains prob-ably in the world." **"And by your sword you shall live."** The mode of life and occupation of the inhabitants were adapted to the country . . . His maintenance would be by the sword, i.e., he will live by war, rapine and free-booting [piracy].[10]

Most important, Esau was already holding a grudge against Jacob. For he said, **"Is he not rightly named Jacob, for he has cheated me these two times?"** This shows that he was keeping count of the wrongs he felt Jacob had done to him.

Hate Becomes 'Everlasting Enmity'

Once Esau realized that the inheritance and blessing had per-manently been given to Jacob, he said, **"So Esau hated Jacob because of the blessing with which his father blessed him, and Esau said in his heart, 'The days of mourning for my father are at hand; then I will kill my brother Jacob.'"**[11]

---

10. C. F. Keil and F Delitzsch, *Commentary of the Old Testament* (Grand Rapids, MI: William B. Eerdmans Publishing Co., reprinted 1983), vol. 1, p. 278.

11. Genesis 27:40 (KJV).

This hatred became an enmity that permeated his descendants. They were primarily called the sons of Edom or the Edomites. They later became known as the Idumaens and established the Herod dynasty spoken of in the New Testament. King Herod the Great who ordered the slaughter of the infants in Bethlehem in order to kill the Messiah was a descendant of Esau. His son, Herod the tetrarch of Galilee, beheaded John the Baptist. They were a vicious lot that gained control over Israel for a short time under Roman sponsorship.

But perhaps the most important factor is this—there is evidence that Esau's descendants not only became part of the Ishmael/Arab race, but also confederated with them against Israel. They certainly were among the warriors who first converted to Islam and helped spread it across the Mediterranean world.

It was through marriage that Esau became part of the Arabs. When Esau observed that his father gave strict orders for Jacob not to marry any of the Canaanite women, and that the two Canaanite wives he had already married grieved Isaac, he sought to please his father. So we read, **"Esau then realized how displeasing the Canaanite women were to his father Isaac; so he went to Ishmael and married Mahalath, the sister of Nebaioth and daughter of Ishmael son of Abraham, in addition to the wives he already had."** [12]

A History of Expanding Hate

Throughout the history of Israel, the Edomites took every opportunity to vent their hatred against them. When Israel came out of captivity from Egypt, the Edomites would not even let them pass through their land. **"Thus Edom refused to give Israel passage through his territory; so Israel turned away from him."** [13] God graciously spared Edom despite the fact this brought great hardship upon Israel.

---

12. Genesis 28:8–9 (NIV).
13. Numbers 20:21 (NKJV).

God Warns Amalek

Amalek, one of the Edomite chiefs, was a persistent enemy of Israel. When he fought against Israel as they came from Egypt, God made this prediction:

> Then the Lord said to Moses, "Write this in a book as a memorial, and recite it to Joshua, that I will utterly blot out the memory of Amalek from under heaven." And Moses built an altar, and named it The Lord is My Banner; and he said, "The Lord has sworn; the Lord will have war against Amalek from generation to generation." [14]

Edom Becomes Larger Symbol

Ezekiel fortold that God will judge all Edom (referring to all Arabs) for appropriating Israel's land. This judgment comes in the last days when God miraculously recalls the Israelites from all the countries where He scattered them. That time is now. God says,

> This is what the Sovereign LORD says: In my burning zeal I have spoken against the rest of the nations, and against all EDOM, for *with glee* and *with malice in their hearts* they made my land their own possession so that they might plunder its pastureland. [15]

God warns Edom again about the judgment that will fall at the coming of the Messiah. The reason is clearly given:

> This is what the LORD says: "For three sins of Edom, even for four, I will not turn back my wrath. *Because he pursued his brother* [Israel] *with a sword, stifling all compassion, because his anger raged continually and his fury flamed unchecked,* I will send fire upon Teman that will consume the fortresses of Bozrah." [16]

---

14. Exodus 17:14–16 (NKJV).

15. Ezekiel 36:5 (NIV), emphasis added.

16. Amos 1:11–12 (NIV), emphasis added.

Psalm 83 prophetically tells us of the final mad attempt by the ancient descendants of Abraham's other sons to destroy Israel. It shows that Edom and Ishmael are linked together and leading the conspiracy to wipe Israel off the earth. Just look at the list of Israel's foes in "the last days". It reads like a "Who's Who" of their ancient enemies.

> **Do not keep silent, O God! Do not hold Your peace, And do not be still, O God! For behold, Your enemies make a tumult; And those who hate You have lifted up their head. They have taken crafty counsel against Your people, and consulted together against Your sheltered ones. They have said, "Come, and let us cut them off from being a nation, that the name of Israel may be remembered no more." For they have consulted together with one consent; they form a confederacy against You: The tents of Edom and the Ishmaelites; Moab and the Hagrites; Gebal, Ammon, and Amalek; Philistia with the inhabitants of Tyre; Assyria also has joined with them; They have helped the children of Lot . . . Who said, "Let us take for ourselves the pastures of God for a possession."** [17]

Edom and the Ishmaelites are the primary Arab people. The descendants of Moab, the Hagrites, Gebal, Ammon, Amalek and Philistia melted in the mixed group that were absorbed by the Arab culture and later converted to Islam. Today, these people make up the nations of Jordan, Saudi Arabia, United Arab Emirates, Oman, and:

- Tyre is now Lebanon.

- Assyria is modern Syria.

- Persia is modern Iran

All of these people are linked together by their common continuous enmity toward Israel.

---

17. Psalm 83:1–12 (NKJV).

In the next chapter, we will examine how this ancient enmity became woven into a religion founded by a direct descendant of Ishmael. We will see how the spread of hatred toward Israel became co-extensive with the spread of this religion.

CHAPTER SIX

The Muslim Genesis

From the beginning, its [Islam's] spread was accomplished through physical violence, bloodshed and war. Violence not only against non-Muslim infidels, but also against fellow Muslims. Much of Islam's spread in the world was the result of traders and Sufi missionaries, this is true. Yet the weaponry—scimatars and sabers—all through the art and symbolism of Islam, makes violence and war a central theme of Islam . . . Mohammad both taught and practiced violence from the beginning.

Abdul Houssain Zarin Koub, Imminent Muslim Scholar[1]

---

1. Zarin Koub was the longtime head of the department of history religion, and philosophy, at the University of Tehran. He has also lectured at Columbia University and elsewhere. His book, *History of Religion,* has been translated into over 60 languages. Zarin Koub's grandfather was one of the founders of Baghdad University.

*The phenomenal and almost unparalleled efflores-
cence (exponential growth) of early Islam was
due in no small measure to the latent powers of the
Bedouins, who, in the words of the Caliph Omar,
"furnished Islam with its raw material."*[2]

---

2. Ibid.

Arab Pre-Islamic History

There is very little history on the sons of Ishmael and Edom, outside of the Bible, prior to the birth of Mohammad and Islam. We know the names of the twelve sons of Ishmael from whom the Arabs primarily descended, but not all twelve tribal lines can be clearly traced. However, the Bible does give a careful genealogy of Ishmael to demonstrate that God kept his promise to him:

> **This is the account of Abraham's son Ishmael, whom Sarah's maidservant, Hagar the Egyptian, bore to Abraham. These are the names of the sons of Ishmael, listed in the order of their birth: Nebaioth the firstborn of Ishmael, Kedar, Adbeel, Mibsam, Mishma, Dumah, Massa, Hadad, Tema, Jetur, Naphish and Kedemah. These were the sons of Ishmael, and these are the names of the twelve tribal rulers according to their settlements and camps. Altogether, Ishmael lived a hundred and thirty-seven years. He breathed his last and died, and he was gathered to his people. His descendants settled in the area from Havilah to Shur, near the border of Egypt, as you go toward Asshur. And they lived [to the east] in hostility toward all their brothers.**[3]

The second son Kedar is the most frequently mentioned son of Ishmael. He became the most powerful and wealthy of all his brothers.

Ezekiel describes the sons of Ishmael as wealthy merchants who traded with the great seafaring empire of Tyre in the fifth and fourth century B.C. before God destroyed it for its wickedness. Ezekiel writes, **"Arabia and all the princes of Kedar were your customers; they did business with you in lambs, rams and goats."**[4] This is part of a prophecy about Tyre's destruction, which was fulfilled by Alexander the Great.

---

3. Genesis 25:12–18.
4. Ezekiel 27:21 (NIV), emphasis added.

We also find some of the descendants of Abraham's sons through his aforementioned concubine Keturah. They are mentioned in the same prophecy as being part of the Arab peoples. They lived in the port cities on the southern tip of the Arabian Peninsula in what is now Yemen and Oman. Ezekiel writes, **"Dedan traded in saddle blankets with you . . . The merchants of Sheba and Raamah traded with you; for your merchandise they exchanged the finest of all kinds of spices and precious stones, and gold."** [5] Sheba and Dedan are grandsons of Abraham through Keturah's second son, Jokshan. [6] Much is written about the spices produced in the southern part of Arabia. Such sought after spices as frankincense and myrrh were produced there.

Isaiah predicts that the wealth of Nebaioth (Ishmael's first born) and Kedar will be offered to the LORD at His Second Coming when He sets up His Kingdom in Israel, **"All Kedar's flocks will be gathered to you, the rams of Nebaioth will serve you; they will be accepted as offerings on my altar, and I will adorn my glorious temple."** [7] This prophecy is significant because it indicates that descendants of Kedar and Nebaioth will continue to exist and prosper until the end of this age.

KORAN'S VIEW OF THIS HISTORY

According to Islamic teaching, Abraham (Arabic—*Ibrahim*) did not stay in Canaan with Isaac nor send his other seven half brothers to the land of the East.

Muslims teach Abraham went to Mecca where he raised all eight sons together. They also believe it was Ishmael—not Isaac—that Abraham offered as a sacrifice on Mount Moriah before the Angel stopped him. They absolutely believe Ishmael was the chosen one of God, not Isaac. This is the basis of their denial of the Biblical Covenants that are specifically confirmed to Abraham

---

5. Ezekiel 27:20, 22 (NIV), emphasis added.

6. Genesis 25:3 (NIV).

7. Isaiah 60:7 (NIV).

through his line of descendants from Isaac, Jacob and his twelve sons. It is on this basis that Muslims claim all the Land of Israel and Jerusalem. Christians view this as a great error because the Old and New Testaments, plus the specific testimony of the Lord Jesus, teach the God of the Bible is the God of Abraham, Isaac and Jacob —not Abraham, Ishmael, Esau and Mohammad.

The Arab's Warring Nature

The writer of Psalm 120 gives insight into the violent nature of the descendants of Kedar, **"Woe to me . . . that I live among the tents of Kedar! Too long have I lived among those who hate peace. I am a man of peace; but when I speak, they are for war."**[8] Both secular and Biblical sources describe the Arabs, especially the sons of Kedar, as a people who continuously fought. This certainly fulfills God's prophecy about the sons of Ishmael that said, **"His hand shall be against everyone, and everyone's hand against him."**

Isaiah has a number of prophetic visions of judgment concerning the nations surrounding and Israel who afflicted them. They are called "Oracles". The following oracle gives insight into the character of the Arabians—particularly Kedar—in the eighth century B.C. This Oracle actually predicted the Assyrian King Sargon's invasion of Arabia in 716 B.C.:

> **An oracle concerning *Arabia*: You caravans of *Dedanites*, who camp in the thickets of Arabia, bring water for the thirsty; you who live in *Tema*, bring food for the fugitives. They flee from the sword, from the drawn sword, from the bent bow and from the heat of battle. This is what the Lord says to me: "Within one year, as a servant bound by contract would count it, all the pomp of *Kedar* will come to an end. The survivors of the bowmen, the warriors of *Kedar*, will be few." The LORD, the God of Israel, has spoken.**[9]

---

8. Psalm 120:5–7 (NIV).

9. Isaiah 21:13–18 (NIV), emphasis added.

As indicated, the sons of Kedar were especially known for being expert archers. Kedar must have learned his skill with the bow and arrow from his father Ishmael, for it is written of him, **"God was with the boy [Ishmael] as he grew up. He lived in the desert and became an [expert] archer."** [10] The northern Arabians fled to the south and were weak for over a century after this invasion.

The Extent of Arab Territory

Keil and Delitzsch link the descendants of Kedar to the wealthy and powerful merchants known as the Nabateans.[11] They ruled the region known by the Chaldeans and Romans as Arabia Petra. Petra, the capitol, was a famous banking city built into a natural fortress in the mountains of Edom. During the Greco-Roman times, this kingdom covered the northern part of the Arabian Peninsula.

Petra was known as the "Lost City" until archeologists redis-covered it in the nineteenth century A.D. The way it was con-structed made it one of the wonders of the ancient world.

Ishmael and his descendants began in the desert of Shur and Havilah in the northwest part of the Arabian Peninsula. From there they continued to expand southward and eastward to extend their borders to where the Peninsula touched ancient Assyria and Babylon. As stated earlier, there is no doubt the Ishmaelites absorbed other people, such as the descendants of Esau/Edom and of Abraham's sons through Keturah. But Biblical history, support-ed by secular history, presents the Ishmaelites as the dominant peo-ple called "the Arabs."

Smith's Bible Dictionary makes this observation:

> The Ishmaelites appear to have entered the peninsula from the northwest. That they spread over the whole of it, and

---

10. Genesis 21:20 (NIV).

11. C. F. Keil and F Delitzsch, *Commentary of the Old Testament* (Grand Rapids, MI: William. B. Eerdmans Publishing Co., reprinted 1983), vol. 1, p. 264.

that the modern nation is predominately Ishmaelite, is asserted by the Arabs . . . they mixed with other Abrahamic peoples; and expanded westwards to Idumaea, where they mixed with Edomites, etc. The tribes sprung from Ishmael have always been governed by petty chiefs or heads of families (sheiks and emirs) . . . though they have in some instances succeeded to those of the Joktanites.[12]

By the first century A.D., Josephus wrote the Arabs were, "dwelling from the Euphrates to the Red Sea."[13] The climate and terrain were so difficult, no foreign invader ever totally conquered them. The only people to ever thrive in the vast desert of Arabia are Arab Bedouin. And as predicted, they have prevailed in defiance of all their brothers, dwelling to their east.

Seventh Century Arabian Culture

It is impossible to understand the Muslim religion apart from understanding the Arabian culture out of which it was born. By the sixth and seventh centuries A.D., the culture, customs and religion of Arabia had become well established. The culture was particularly concentrated in a key city of the great Arabian caravan route called Mecca. Virtually everything Mohammad included in the Koran and the Muslim religion can be traced to existing traditions of that time and place.

ORGANIZATION OF ARABIAN SOCIETY AND GOVERNMENT

The Arabians began as nomadic tribes or clans in the deserts. They were known as Bedouins. Clan organization is the basis of the Arab Bedouin society. There is one supreme chief over the clan called a Sheik. The clan is composed of many families. A family unit dwelt in one tent. All members of the same clan consider each other as of one blood; submit to the authority of but one chief, the

12. William Smith, *Smith's Bible Dictionary*, (New York: Family Library).

13. Josephus, *Antiquities*, i. 12, 4.

senior member of the clan; and use one battle cry. Blood relation-ship—real or fictitious (clan kinship may be acquired by sucking a few drops of a member's blood) furnishes the cohesive element in tribal organization.

The tent, household goods and all personal items such as camels, horses, livestock and weapons are individual property. But water sources, pasturage and tillable land are the common proper-ty of the tribe.

There is a certain amount of freedom and individuality within the clan, but in all corporate clan decisions and actions, the Sheik has the final word. The highest hope of a clan member was for a "benevolent dictator".

This is why there is such an inevitable cultural collision with the West. The Arabians have no concept of a democratic govern-ment, where leaders are elected and responsible to the will of the people. Their pattern of government has always been an autocrat-ic dictator reigning over subjects. As we will see, the Islamic Fundamentalist views democracy as a threat to the Muslim religion.

VIOLENCE ENDEMIC TO ARABIAN CULTURE

Violence has been a continual fact of life for the Arabs. This is a common thread that runs through historical accounts of their culture. Philip Hitti summarized this fact well:

> "The RAID or *ghazw* . . . is raised by the economic and social conditions of desert life to the rank of a national institution. *It lies at the base of the economic structure of Bedouin pastoral society. In desert land, where the fighting mood is a chronic mental condition,* raiding is one of the few manly occupations. An early Arab poet gave expres-sion to the guiding principle of such life in two verses: 'Our business is to make raids on the enemy, on our neighbor and on our own brother, in case we find none to raid but a brother!'" [14]

---

14. Philip K. Hitti, *The Arabs: A Short History* (Washington DC: Regnery Publishing, Inc., 1996), emphasis added, <http://www.oneworldmagazine.org/focus/deserts/toc.htm>.

How perfectly God's prophecy about the sons of Ishmael fits: **"His hand shall be against everyone, and everyone's hand against him."** Also, God's prediction concerning the other major part of the Arab people, the sons of Edom from Esau: **"Your dwelling will be away from the earth's richness, away from the dew of heaven above. You will live by the sword . . ."** [15] The Edomites first lived in the mountains of Seir, but over the centuries, many were forced to flee to the desert of Arabia where there is little "richness of earth or dew from heaven." They have always lived by the sword.

It is startling that the Arabic language has almost a thousand names and synonyms for *sword*. The only other word in Arabic that can rival for multiple names is *camel*. Both the sword and the camel were considered essential for life in the Arabian culture. It is important to note today how many Arab countries have the insignia of the sword in their national logos.

The Arabian Religion
THE 'DAYS OF IGNORANCE'

Long before the founding of Islam, in what was known as the "Days of Ignorance," the Arabs lost faith in the one true God, whom their forefathers Ishmael, Esau and the sons of Keturah knew. They degenerated into polytheism and worshiped "holy" rocks and trees. These objects were not deemed sacred because they were in themselves so, but because it was believed they were indwelt by *spirit beings* called "jinns" (later known as "genies").

Arabs believed (and noted in the Koran and Hadith) that "jinns" were a category of spirit creatures halfway between angels and men. They believed they can be good or bad, though most are considered to be malicious. They can possess animals and inanimate things such as rocks, trees, wells, etc. Jinns were adopted into Muslim theology and the Koran. Legends about jinns or genies are resplendent in Arab legends—such as the genie in the bottle, etc.

---

15. Genesis 26:39–40 (NIV).

During this period, Mecca became Islam's most important religious center. It was a major oasis on the main caravan route from earliest times. Mecca developed first because it was the site of the sacred Zamzam Well, which Arabs believe God revealed to Abraham and Ishmael.

THE KABAH

Mecca's greatest significance came from being the site of the special religious alter known as the Kabah. It is a 50-foot cubic structure of gray stone and marble. Positioned so that its corners correspond with the four points of the compass, the Kabah contained 360 idols—one for each of the lunar calendar days.

The cornerstone of the Kabah was the sacred Black Stone. It is a meteorite of very ancient origin. It was and is believed to have the power to absorb sin from the one who kisses it. Arabs believe that the Black Stone is a god who protects their tribes.

THE HIERARCHY OF GODS

In the Arab pantheon of gods, five were most important in their hierarchy. There were Uzza, Allat, Manat, and Hubal. The first three were female, which formed a tritheistic relationship. On the other hand, Hubal was a male Moon deity. He is believed to originated in Babylon.

It is Hubal that is represented in the Hilal, Islam's symbol of the Crescent Moon. The star is believed to represent Uzza, the Morning Star goddess. Hubal was also believed to be the guardian of the Kabah.

The fifth and highest of all deities was called "Allah." He was worshiped as the supreme creator as well as the "father " of the tritheistic female goddesses.

THE MECCA PILGRIMAGE

Mecca, with the Kabah, the sacred Zamzam Well and the presence of the highest deities, became the religious vortex of the Arabian Peninsula. Arabs from all over began to come on pilgrimages to Mecca—long before Mohammad.

It was because of the lucrative business brought by the pilgrims that possessing the guardianship of the sacred Kabah and Zamzam Well became a prize to be sought.

RIVALRY FOR HOLY SITES BEGINS

From approximately 100 B.C., the Kabah and its sacred well were under the control of a tribe known as the Beni Jurham. In about the third century A.D., they seem to have been driven out and replaced by an Ishmaelite tribe known as the Khuzaa.

Then in about A.D. 235, Fihr, the leader of another Ishmaelite tribe, the Quraysh, married the daughter of the Khuzaa tribal chief. Later, in about A.D. 420, Qusai, a descendant of Fihr, married the daughter of another Khuzaa chief of Mecca. Although he was not of the Khuzaa tribe, Qusai made himself virtually indispensable to his father-in-law, who was guardian of the Kabah. As a result, Qusai was given the custodianship of the coveted sacred keys of the Kabah.

When the Khuzaa died, Qusai claimed custody of the Kabah for the Quraysh. One of his first acts was to relegate the Khuzaa clan to a subordinate position. Qusai ordered the building of a semi-permanent housing around the Kabah. He also shrewdly restructured the tribal social order. He instituted tribal council meetings and a hall was built near the Kabah for this purpose.

THE QURAYSH TRIBAL RELIGION

It was not coincidental that the Quraysh Tribe from which Mohammad's family came was addicted to the cult of the moon god, Allah. They witnessed the pilgrims coming to Mecca every year to worship, circling the Kabah seven times, kissing the Black

Stone (considered their special tribal talisman that guaranteed their protection and blessing), and then running down to the near-by Wadi to throw stones at the devil. Mohammad was destined to grow up with these religious traditions. So it cannot be an accident that all of these religious traditions are prominent in the Muslim religion, which he supposedly received by original, divine revelation.

THE QURAYSH TRIBE PREVAILS

The rivalries continued through the centuries. But, important to our interest, the Quraysh tribe prevailed as guardians of Mecca's holy sites by the sixth century A.D. Within the Quraysh tribe, a man named Hashim married a woman named Selma, who gave birth to a son, Abdul al-Mut-Talib. Abdul had seven sons— Harith, Talib, Lahab, Jahal, Abbas, Hamza and Abdullah.

Abdullah married Amina, who was a descendant of Qusai's brother Zuhra. Abdullah and Amina gave birth to a son whom they named Mohammad. With this event, the entire history of the Arab people was about to take a paradigm shift.

CHAPTER SEVEN

Mohammad, The Great Enigma

"But even though we, or an angel from heaven, should preach to you a gospel contrary to that which we have preached to you, let him be accursed. As we have said before, so I say again now, if any man is preaching to you a gospel contrary to that which you received, let him be accursed."

THE APOSTLE PAUL[1]

"Wonderful Originator of the heavens and the earth! HOW COULD HE HAVE A SON when he has no consort . . . Follow what is revealed to you from your Lord; THERE IS NO GOD BUT HE; and withdraw from the polytheists [i.e., Christians]."

THE KORAN[2]

---

1. Galatians 1:8–9.

2. Surah 6.102, 106, emphasis added.

The word *enigma* is defined as, "A mystery: somebody or something that is not easily explained or understood."[3] This word certainly applies to Mohammad. He is a conundrum of history. Indeed, apart from the acceptance that a supernatural being worked in and through him, there is no way to comprehend him.

- How did an orphan become the greatest Arab leader of all time?

- How could an illiterate man become the author of a book that is the pinnacle of classic Arabic — the most beautiful and majestic of all Arabic literature?

- How is it possible one who was, as a child thought to be either insane or demon-possessed, became the founder of the second largest religion on earth?

- How did a man who was admittedly both violent and sensual become one of the most revered religious leaders in history?

This is why I say Mohammad is an "enigma"—apart from the working of supernatural forces, it is impossible to explain him.

You can worship him as God's last and greatest Prophet, or you can reject him as a false prophet—but you cannot ignore him. This one man is solely responsible for the Arabs exploding out of the Arabian Peninsula and in less than 100 years conquering lands from the Atlantic to the borders of China, from North Africa to Spain and into the gates of Vienna in Europe. If the Muslim hoards had not been stopped by the Frankish king, Charles Martel, at the Battle of Tours in A.D. 732, all of Europe would have fallen under Islam's control.

The Birth Of Mohammad

Mohammad was born around A.D. 570 and died in July of A.D. 632. His father was from the Quraysh tribe. This tribe gained much

---

3. *Microsoft Encarta World Dictionary*, s.v. "enigma".

power and influence, both for their commercial activity in Mecca, and because they were the guardians of the sacred well and the Kabah with its black meteorite cornerstone. They enjoyed prestige, influence and profit because of the continuous religious pilgrimages all Arabia made to the Meccan "holy sites."

Mohammad's father was Abdallah, the son of Abd al-Muttalib by Fatima bint 'Amr of the Quraysh clan of the Banu Makhzum. Abdallah was reputed to be quite handsome. Marriages were strategically calculated for political and economic goals, and Abd al-Muttalib was seeking an alliance with the Banu Zuhra (Shura) clan. Thus he arranged for Amina bint Wahb to marry his son, Abdallah.

The 'Visitations' Begin

Abdallah and his new wife soon became the parents of a son whom they named Mohammad. According to consistent historical witnesses, Mohammad had a strange childhood, one marked by the presence of many different caretakers and "visitations of spirits and angels."

We may gain an important insight into Mohammad from a description given of his mother. Muslim scholar Robert Morey writes:

> Mohammad's mother, Aminah, was of an excitable nature and often claimed that she was visited by spirits, or jinns. She also at times claimed to have visions and religious experiences. Mohammad's mother was involved in what we call today the "occult arts," and this basic orientation is thought by some scholars to have been inherited by her son.[4]

From birth, Amina feared for the infant's health in the crowded conditions of Mecca. So she did what Quraysh mothers with means customarily did—she hired a nurse from one of the Bedouin tribes to take him into "the healthy air of the desert."[5]

---

4. Robert Morey, *Islamic Invasion*, (Eugene, OR: Harvest House Publishers, 1992) p. 71.

5. Dr. Anis A. Shorrosh, *Islam Revealed*, (Knoxville, TN: Thomas Nelson Publishers, 1988), p. 48

Mohammad was entrusted to a Bedouin woman named Halima, who nursed the infant until he was two before bringing him back to Amina. Delighted with his healthy look, Mohammad's mother said, "Take the child with thee back again, for much do I fear for him the unwholesome air of Mecca."[6] So Halima took him back. After two more years she returned again, but this time she was troubled. The child had experienced numerous fits, which made Halima think he was demon-possessed. Amina, however, pleaded with her to carry him back once more. But after subsequent epileptic fits and "spirit visitations", Halima returned him to his mother when he was five and refused to take him back. Mohammad always remembered Halima with great affection.

Author Robert Payne investigates in detail the incident that caused Halima to return Mohammad at age five. Payne says:

> Mohammad experienced the first of his "visitations" while he was walking in a field with one of Halima's sons. He suddenly fell down shouting that "two men in white garments" were splitting open his belly. When later asked by Halima what happened, he said "two angels had cut open his belly searching for something."[7]

According to Mohammad's own testimony, he experienced these sorts of "visitations" for the rest of his life.

Mohammad's Early Tragedies

Abdullah, Mohammad's father, died before he was five while he was under Halima's care. One year after he was returned to his mother, she also died. So Mohammad became an orphan at the vulnerable age of six. He was then entrusted to the care of his seventy-year-old grandfather and his mother's slave girl, Umm Ayan.

When Mohammad turned 12, his grandfather died. His uncle Abu Talib took him under his care and began taking him on long

---

6. Shorrosh, *Islam Revealed*, p. 48.

7. Robert Payne, *The Holy Sword* (Collier Books, 1962), p. 84.

caravan journeys to Damascus and other great cities of the Middle East. During this time he apprenticed in the merchant trade. He continued working in the trade until he was twenty-five.

Mohammad Takes A Wife

When Mohammad turned 25, his uncle suggested that he go to work for a rich widow merchant in Mecca named Khadija. He was hired to accompany her merchant caravan to Syria, which he did several times. Although she was 40 years of age, widowed twice and had three daughters, they married. Together they had two sons, Abdullah and Qusim, and a daughter named Fatima. Tragically, the two boys died in infancy.

As mentioned before, Mohammad exhibited mystic tendencies and was very religious from an early age. Khadija's wealth gave him the opportunity to take long retreats into the hills around Mecca for uninterrupted periods of religious meditation. However, these religious quests did not bring him inner peace. His frequent excursions into the desert produced a "spiritual anxiety" that was not just reflected in his personality, but in the religion he founded.

Historians have sought to analyze Mohammad's complex temperament because it is so reflected in the religion he founded. Sir Norman Anderson observed:

> He would retire to caves for seclusion and meditation. He frequently practiced fasting; and he was prone to dreams. His character seems to have been a strange mixture. He was a poet rather than a theologian; a master improviser rather than a systematic thinker . . . He was generous, resolute, genial and astute: a shrewd judge and a born leader of men. He could however, be cruel and vindictive to his enemies; he could stop to assassinate; and he was undeniably sensual.[8]

---

8. Sir Norman Anderson, *The World's Religions*, (Grand Rapids, MI.: William B. Eerdmans Publishers, 1976), p. 52.

Robert Payne notes the contradictory traits within his nature:

> It is worthwhile to pause for a moment before the quite astonishing polarity of Mohammad's mind. *Violence and gentleness were at war within him.* Sometimes he gives the appearance of living simultaneously in two worlds, at one and the same moment seeing the world about to be destroyed by the flames of God and in the state of divine peace . . .[9]

These two antithetical traits of violence and gentleness equally existing together in his soul are what made Mohammad such a complex person. He seems to have been able to exert either trait at any moment without any personal awareness of contradiction. He also held severe grudges toward those who rejected his religious claims, as the Jews and the Christians would learn.

Dr. Shorrosh gives this interesting description of Mohammad's appearance based on eyewitness accounts:

> As an adult, Mohammad was somewhat above middle height, with a lean but commanding figure. His head was massive, with a broad and noble forehead. He had thick black hair, slightly curling which hung over his ears; his eyes were large, black and piercing; his eyebrows arched and joined; his nose high and aquiline; and he had a long bushy beard. When he was excited, the veins would swell across his forehead. His eyes were often bloodshot and always restless. Decision marked his every movement. He used to walk so rapidly that his followers half ran behind him and could hardly keep up with him.[10]

'The Night of Power'—It All Begins

In A.D. 610, when Mohammad was 40, he had a visitation that would come to be known as "The Night of Power." It was this extraordinary experience that finally convinced Mohammad he was called as God's prophet and apostle. Muslims believe Allah

---

9. Payne, *The Holy Sword*, p. 84, emphasis added.

10. Shorrosh, *Islam Revealed*, p. 50.

began revealing the true religion of Islam that night.

According to Islam, this beginning revelation came to Mohammad in the form of "a gracious and mighty messenger, held in honor by the Lord of the Throne." The messenger appeared to him in a cave on Mount Ararat, which overlooks the Hijaz Valley in eastern Arabia in the vicinity of Mecca.

"Proclaim!" the angel commanded three times. Dazzled, Mohammad asked, "What shall I proclaim?" The angel replied, "Proclaim in the name of your Lord who created, created man from clots of blood! Proclaim! Your Lord who created the most bountiful one, who by the pen taught man what he did not know."

At this point, Muslim scholars believe Mohammad saw himself as more of a reformer and restorer than a founder of a new religion. Mohammad believed he was sent to re-establish monotheism as it had originally been revealed. He believed the original recipients—Jews and Christians—had corrupted God's true revelation. In the Koran, he even calls Jews "the people of the Book."

This is the fundamental belief that guaranteed a collision with Judaism and Christianity. In one fell swoop, it dismisses the Bible as a book laced with lies and fraud introduced by Jews and Christians. Muslims teach that Jews—and to a lesser degree Christians—deliberately perverted the original revelation from God to make themselves the recipients of God's covenants and blessings.

Here are a few examples of this teaching in the Koran:

> O followers of the Book (Jews)! Indeed Our Apostle has come to you making clear to you much of what you concealed of the Book and passing over much; indeed, there has come to you light and a clear Book from Allah (i.e. the Koran); With it Allah guides him who will follow His pleasure into the ways of safety and brings them out of utter darkness into light by His will and guides them to the right path.[11]

---

11. Surah 5.15, 16.

O you who believe! Do not take the Jews and the Christians for friends; they are friends of each other; and whoever amongst you takes them for a friend, then surely he is one of them; surely Allah does not guide these unjust people.[12]

Mode of Mohammad's Revelations

The mode in which Mohammad received subsequent revelations from Allah is uniformly recorded in Muslim tradition. When Mohammad was about to receive a revelation he would fall down on the ground, his body would begin to jerk, his eyes would roll backward and he would perspire profusely. His followers would cover him with a blanket during these "visitations."

The revelations occurred when Mohammad went into a trancelike state. When he would come out of it, he would begin to proclaim what had been transmitted to him.

As we view this description today, it would seem to be an epileptic seizure. Dr. Morey makes an astute observation about this:

What must be remembered is that in the Arab culture of Mohammad's day, epileptic seizures were interpreted as a religious sign of either demonic possession or divine visitation.

Muhammad initially considered both options as possible interpretations of his experience. At first he worried about the possibility that he was demon possessed. This led him to attempt to commit suicide.

But his devoted wife was able to stop him from committing suicide by persuading him that he was such a good man that he could not possibly be demon possessed.[13]

Whatever caused these trancelike states, it is clear the revelations he received were from a supernatural source. The real ques-

12. Surah 5.51.

13. Morey, *Islamic Invasion*, p. 72.

tion is not so much about the method of revelation, but its origin. From a Christian viewpoint, there are only two sources of the supernatural: The God of the Bible, and **"the god of this world"** [14] who is also described as **"an angel of light."** [15]

Testing Supernatural Sources

The Bible offers tests to prove its authenticity as a message from God. Moses, the first writing Prophet from God, was given a test to prove whether a message or a prophet was truly from God:

> **But the prophet who shall speak a word presumptuously in My name which I have not commanded him to speak, or which he shall speak in the name of other gods, that prophet shall die.**
>
> **And you may say in your heart, 'How shall we know the word which the Lord has not spoken?' When a prophet speaks in the name of the Lord, if the thing does not come about or come true, that is the thing which the Lord has not spoken. The prophet has spoken it presumptuously; you shall not be afraid of him.** [16]

Here, God teaches that the true prophet will make detailed predictions about the future that can be proven or disproven. If the prophecies *all* come true, then the people are to heed his words as the Word of God. If any part of his prophecy did not come true, they were to stone the person as a false prophet and destroy his message.

This is why of all the books written in Israel's history (and there were others), *only* the ones that are genuine were preserved in the canon of Scripture. And this was in spite of the fact that these books frequently condemned the people's sinful behavior from the king to the peasant. Each prophet proved himself true by fulfilled prophecy. The Israelites had every reason to destroy these unpopular messages, some even predicted the destruction of the

---

14. 2 Cornithians 4:3

15. 2 Cornithians 11:14

16. Deuteronomy 18:19–22.

nation for its sin. But they did not dare destroy that which was proven to be God's word.

The Koran, on the other hand, has no such proofs with which to authenticate its divine origin. Instead, the believer is exhorted not to question and to kill anyone who does. Blind, unquestioning belief is demanded.

Islamic Revelation vs. Biblical Inspiration

The concept of how the divine message of the Koran was received is very different from how the approximately 40 writers of the Bible received theirs. The Arabic word for "revelation" means *handed down*. Muslims believe the Koran did not come "through" any man, not even Mohammad. They believe the message came directly from Allah to the angel Gabriel, who passed it to Mohammad as a total package, "intact" with no human involvement or interaction. Additionally, the Koran was not written down until years after Mohammad's death.

The Bible claims something very different about itself. It teaches that all Scriptures are **"God-breathed"** (literal meaning of Θεοπνευστος),[17] meaning every word of the Bible has God's direct inspiration upon it.

The Bible further claims that it is not the product of man's interpretation:

> **Above all, you must understand that no prophecy of Scripture came about by the prophet's own interpretation. For prophecy never had its origin in the will of man, but men spoke from God as they were carried along by the Holy Spirit.**[18]

The word translated **"carried along"** is a nautical term, referring to the wind blowing a sailboat.

---

17. See 2 Timothy 3:16–17.
18. 2 Peter 1:20–21 (NIV).

The idea is that God so moved upon specially chosen men, so they communicated exactly what He wanted to say, but without setting aside their individuality or background.

The Apostle Paul adds that the Holy Spirit so moved upon the minds of the writers that what they reduced to writing was in *the very words* God desired:

> **Now we have received, not the spirit of the world, but the Spirit who is from God, that we might know the things freely given to us by God, which things we also speak, not in words taught by human wisdom, but in those taught by the Spirit, combining spiritual thoughts with spiritual words.**[19]

The Bible is Unique

The great miracle of the Bible is that some forty authors from different times and places produced a Holy Book that has one homogenous, cohesive and consistent message. Its Divine origin is unmistakeable. It does not contradict nature, history or any proven factors of science, though primitive men wrote it. The Bible contains hundreds of prophecies that have all been fulfilled with 100 percent accuracy and are historical record. No other book can compare with that record.

Because the Holy Spirit combined **"spiritual thoughts with spiritual words"**, it does not make sense to someone who is "spiritually dead." The Bible teaches that all mankind are born physically alive, but spiritually dead. This is why Jesus told a religious scholar of his day that unless a man is "born again spiritually", he cannot understand the kingdom of God.

The Apostle Paul explains it this way:

> **But a natural man does not accept the things of the Spirit of God; for they are foolishness to him, and he cannot**

---

19. 1 Corinthians 2:12–13.

understand them, because they are spiritually appraised [understood].[20]

The Koran does not speak on such topics. As a matter of fact, the Koran does not deal with the great issues of man's sin and the need for a righteous God to have a just basis upon which to forgive man.

Mohammad Begins To Preach

After the initial appearance of the angel, whom Mohammad later identified as Gabriel, Mohammad went through another period of self-doubt, depression and thoughts of death.

He finally decided to commit suicide. He set out to end it all, but along the way he fell into another trance. While in this trance he had a vision in which he was told he must not end his life because he was truly called to be God's special messenger.

Khadija's Key Role

It is at this point that Khadija played a pivotal role in Mohammad's life. When he fully shared with her the anguish and doubt he had about his call from God, she strongly encouraged him. She dismissed his fears of being demon-possessed as an absolute impossibility because he was such a good person. She vehemently believed that he was called of God as his Prophet and Apostle and kept assuring him of that.

Khadija then urged Mohammad to begin preaching the message he received from the angel to his family and friends. All of his first converts were family members.

Opposition and Rejection

When the public heard about Mohammad's new teaching, op-

---

20. 1 Corinthians 2:14.

position started almost at once. The people of Mecca rejected and ridiculed his message. Even some family members turned against him.

Robert Morey explains the crisis that arose in Mohammad at this point:

> In order to appease his pagan family members and the members of the Quraysh tribe, he decided that the best thing he could do was to agree with tradition—that it was perfectly proper to pray to and worship the three daughters of Allah: Al-Lat, Al-Uzza and Manat.
>
> This led to the famous "satanic verses" in which Mohammad in a moment of weakness and supposedly under the inspiration of Satan (according to early Muslim authorities) succumbed to the temptation to appease the pagan mobs in Mecca.
>
> The literature on the "satanic verses" is so vast that an entire volume could be written just on this one issue. Every general and Islamic reference work, Muslim or Western, deals with it as well as all the biographies of Mohammad.
>
> The story of Mohammad's temporary appeasement of the pagans by allowing them their polytheism cannot be ignored or denied. It is a fact of history that is supported by all Middle East scholars, Western and Muslim.[21]

The 'Yathrib Rebuke'

Later, when the disciples of Yathrib (Medina) heard of these compromises with polytheism, there was a very concerned reaction. They came to Mecca and rebuked Mohammad. After consulting with them, he reverted back to the original message of monotheism and said Allah had now forbidden worship of the three goddesses. He explained this clear contradiction by saying that Allah could "abrogate" or cancel a previous revelation.

Later, Mohammad claimed that the angel Gabriel appeared to

---

21. Morey, *Islamic Invasion*, p. 78–79.

him and rebuked him for allowing Satan to deceive him into condoning the Meccan's worship of the three goddesses.

This produced no end of problems for Mohammad, since these goddesses were believed to be the "daughters of Allah." This contradicted what became the very heart of the Islamic faith—"There is no God but Allah." Particularly in view of the many Koranic verses that say Jesus cannot be the Son of God because Allah has no offspring. So the "revelations" Mohammad received during this time were never included in the written version of the Koran. They came to be called "the Satanic Verses." In our era, the Ayatollahs of Iran have issued a death sentence against a Muslim named Salman Rushdie for daring to write a book about these verses.

Meccan Attack

The people of Mecca used this situation against Mohammad to the fullest. They mocked and ridiculed him for attacking the gods of Arabia, especially since those dieties brought the lucrative pilgrim tours to Mecca. They used Mohammad's vacillating messages from Allah to mock the message in its entirety.

The hostility of the Meccans became so great that they drove Mohammad out of Mecca and he fled to Ta-if. He did not receive a good response there so he tried to return to Mecca

On the way back to Mecca, Mohammad claims in the Koran that he preached to the jinns and converted them. Concerning this, the Koran says:

> Say: It has been revealed to me that a party of the jinn listened, and they said: Surely we have heard a wonderful Quran [proclamation], guiding to the right way, so we believe in it, and we will not set up any one with our Lord: And that He—exalted be the majesty of our Lord—has not taken a consort, nor a son . . ."[22]

---

22. Surah 73.1–3.

This important claim is also in Surah 46.29–35 and in 73.1–28. By this revelation, Mohammad claims even the spirits (jinns) that indwell the sacred rocks, trees and water sources believed his message. Notice how Mohammad corrects his previous statements about Allah. He now proclaims Allah does not have a "consort", such as the three goddesses; nor does he have a son, such as Jesus Christ.

When Mohammad arrived again in Mecca, he found there was now organized hostility against him and his message. The merchants were now involved and were out to protect their financial interests. They rightly feared that Mohammad's renewed monotheistic attacks against the idols housed in the Kabah would threaten their leadership, the pilgrimages to Mecca, and their livelihood.

The animosity grew so intense against Mohammad and his followers that some Meccans would have killed him. So he fled with some 200 followers to Yathrib. This famous escape in A.D. 622 became known as the "Hegira."

Yathrib Becomes Medina

It took Mohammad, and his converts, about ten days to reach Yathrib. When he arrived, the oasis city extended him a lavish welcome. They greatly honored him and even changed the city's name to *Madinat-al-Nabi*, which means "the City of the Prophet." The shortened form of this name is simply "Medina."

In Medina, Mohammad established his first Islamic Theocracy, which would become a model for all future Islamic law and government. Medina also became Mohammad's military base from which strategic attacks were launched against the Meccan army and their caravans.

During this period, Mohammad developed his most important Islamic doctrines. Indeed Medina became the model for his "ideal Islamic culture" that would be spread to the world. We will see in the next chapter how the doctrines and traditions developed here are a threat to us today.

CHAPTER EIGHT

The Medina Legacy: Jihad Against Jews

"And those of the People of the Book (Jews) who aided them (Meccan invaders)—Allah did take them down from their strongholds and cast terror into their hearts. So that some you slew and others you took captive. And He [Allah] made you masters of their land, their houses and their goods, and of a land which you have not yet trodden. Truly Allah has power over all things."

THE KORAN

---

1. Surah 33.26-27, translated by Abuallah Yusef Ali.

The Jews of Arabia

A round 1400 B.C., over 2000 years before the first Muslim invasion of Palestina (as the Romans renamed it), Israel was already established as a nation.

A civil war split Israel into two nations during the time of Rehoboam, Soloman's son. The ten tribes of the northern land known as Samaria called themselves Israel. The southern tribes of Judah, Benjamin and Levi became known as the kingdom of Judah, from which the name "Jew" came.

The Assyrian Dispersion

Israel entered a continuous spiral of apostasy until Jehovah finally sent the Assyrians to destroy them in 721 B.C. The survivors of the ten tribes were taken captive into Assyria.

Why is this necessary to know? Because some of the survivors of this dispersion fled to Arabia and settled there. Arabist scholar Alfred Guillaume observes that the Israelites probably settled in Arabia at the time of the fall of Samaria in 721 B.C. He writes, ". . . It is not impossible that some Jewish settlements in Arabia were due to fugitives fleeing from the old northern capitol of the Hebrews."[2]

The Babylonian Dispersion

The southern kingdom of Judah experienced intermittent revivals, but finally fell into the same apostasy as the Samarian Kingdom. Though Judah was repeatedly warned, they did not listen.

> **The LORD, the God of their fathers, sent word to them through his messengers again and again, because he had pity on his people and on his dwelling place. But they mocked God's messengers, despised his words and scoffed at his prophets until the wrath of the LORD was**

---

2. Alfred Guillaume, *Islam* (Baltimore: Penguin Books, 1954), pp. 10–11.

aroused against his people and there was no remedy. He brought up against them the king of the Babylonians, who killed their young men with the sword in the sanctuary, and spared neither young man nor young woman, old man or aged. God handed all of them over to Nebuchadnezzar. He carried to Babylon all the articles from the temple of God, both large and small, and the treasures of the LORD's temple and the treasures of the king and his officials. They set fire to God's temple and broke down the wall of Jerusalem; they burned all the palaces and destroyed everything of value there. He carried into exile to Babylon the remnant, who escaped from the sword, and they became servants to him and his sons until the kingdom of Persia came to power. The land enjoyed its Sabbath rests; all the time of its desolation it rested, until the seventy years were completed in fulfillment of the word of the LORD spoken by Jeremiah.[3]

This is one of the many amazing prophecies in the Bible. Even the number of years the Jews would be held captive against their will was predicted by the prophet Jeremiah and fulfilled to the day. The Babylonian destruction itself was predicted by Isaiah 150 years before it happened:

Then Isaiah said to Hezekiah, "Hear the word of the LORD Almighty: The time will surely come when everything in your palace, and all that your fathers have stored up until this day, will be carried off to Babylon. Nothing will be left, says the LORD. And some of your descendants, your own flesh and blood who will be born to you, will be taken away, and they will become eunuchs in the palace of the king of Babylon."[4]

The Bible records that not all of the Jews were taken to Babylon. A few were left in Judea by the Babylonians to maintain the land. Some were able to flee to Egypt and others to Arabia. In 1949, after the birth of the state of Israel, Israelis rescued the Yemenite Jews from the wrath of the Muslims. Known as "the

---

3. 2 Chronicles 36:15–21 (NIV).
4. Isaiah 39:5–7 (NIV).

wings of eagles," they were all airlifted to Israel. These Yemenite Jews trace their origins in Arabia back 2,500 years, during the time of the Babylonian invasion.

The Roman Dispersion

The greatest flood of Jewish refugees resulted from the initial Roman destruction of Jerusalem and Judea in A.D. 70, and continued for some 150 years. During this time, the Romans fought off different Jewish guerilla-style wars that tried to reclaim Jerusalem. Finally, the Jewish resistance was totally crushed. Some survivors stayed on in Israel while others fled.

Guillaume is certain that "in the first and second centuries A.D., Arabia offered a near asylum" to the Jew who had been victimized by the "utterly ruthless" Romans.

"Yathrib" (Medina) Was Established by Jews

Joan Peters quotes a vital insight by Bernard Lewis,

> In the Arabian land considered by many to be "purely Arab," the land which would spawn Islam many centuries later, numbers of Jewish and Christian settlements were established in different parts of Arabia, both spreading Aramaic and Hellenistic culture. The chief southern Arabian Christian centre was in Najran, where a relatively advanced political life was developed. Jews and Judaized Arabs were everywhere, especially in Yathrib later named Medina. They were mainly agriculturists and artisans.[5]

The second holiest city in the Islamic world was first established by Jews, an amazing fact confirmed by historical sources. How often do we hear or read about this in history? The story of

---

5. Bernard Lewis, *The Arabs in History*, rev. ed. (New York, Evanston, San Francisco, London: Harper-Colophon Books, 1966), pp. 31–32, quoted in Joan Peters, *From Time Immemorial* (New York, N.Y.: Harper & Row, 1984), p. 142.

widespread Jewish settlement in pre-Islamic Arabia is certainly one of the world's best-kept secrets.

The First Palestinian Refugees

"Thus," writes historian Joan Peters, "evolved the flight of the first 'Palestinian refugees'—the Judeans, or Jews."[6] It is extremely important to understand how the early Jewish settlements came to Arabia. These Jewish refugees are seldom discussed, yet understanding what happened to them is critical to understanding today's Middle East crisis.

You may ask why is this important? Because the pattern of action that developed toward the Jews in Arabia established the Islamic tradition that has been followed ever since.

Before Mohammad's time, the comparative wealth of Medina, thanks to the hard-working, industrious Jewish refuges, attracted many pagan Arabs. They came for the jobs, the markets and the commercial opportunities.[7] Again, this pattern was first established in Medina. We will see it repeated in subsequent chapters regarding the nineteenth and twentieth century "Palestine."

It is important to know that Judaism was very popular in parts of Arabia before the birth of Mohammad. Guillaume writes:

> At the dawn of Islam the Jews dominated the economic life of the Hijaz (the sacred eastern section of Arabia that contains Medina and Mecca). They held all of the best land. . . . At Medina they must have formed at least half of the population. There was also a Jewish settlement to the north of the Gulf of Aqaba. . . . What is important is to note that the Jews of the Hijaz made many proselytes (or converts) among the Arab tribesmen.[8]

Guillaume suggests the prosperity of the Jews was due to their

---

6. Peters, *From Time Immemorial*, p. 141.

7. Ibid.

8. Guillaume, *Islam*, pp. 11–12.

superior farming abilities and technology. The first "Palestinian refugees"—the Jews—had quickly become large landowners and controllers of Arabian finance and trade. This success led to the Jews becoming a stumbling block to their envious Arab neighbors —especially in Medina, or Yathrib, as it was then called.[9]

Enter Muhammad

It was into this historical context that Mohammad launched his ministry. As cited in the last chapter, Mohammad's zealous crusade against polytheism made him increasingly unpopular in his hometown of Mecca. When they tried to kill him, he and his disciples fled to Yathrib.

Not surprisingly, the Jews of Yathrib did not accept Mohammad's claim of being a Prophet. Mohammad's tried to win the Jews over by representing himself as simply a teacher of the creed of Abraham. He even adopted the Jewish Sabbath, some dietary laws and initially required prayer toward Jerusalem rather than Mecca.[10]

Believe or Be Beheaded

The Jews, however, were not deceived and refused to acknowledge him as anything but a false prophet. This infuriated Mohammad. He turned to what would become his standard pattern—the sword. He marched against this Jewish tribe and besieged their village. When they surrendered and came out one by one, they were beheaded. The first Muslim massacre was executed on the Jews. The pattern of "confess Islam or face the sword" was established.

Mohammad was anxious to spread Islam beyond Medina. After dealing with the Jews, who had not only rejected but also opposed him, he began to train his disciples as warriors and developed a new strategy for defending Medina. He had them dig a long, deep

---

9. Ibid.

10. Robert Morey, *The Islamic Invasion*, (Eugene, OR: Harvest House Publishers, 1992), p. 82.

trench along the side of the city where the Meccans were expected to attack.

The Battle of the Trench

Although simple by modern standards, this strategy was totally innovative in seventh century Arabia. Unable to get beyond the trench, the Meccan army laid siege to Medina.

Some of the surviving Jewish citizens within the city seized this opportunity to attack Mohammad's army from behind. He had to divide his army to deal with the two-front battle. But a sand storm suddenly struck and forced the Meccans to pull back. Then the Muslims turned their army upon the Jews and slaughtered them.

The Battle of the Trench is commemorated as one of the most decisive and critical events in the formative stages of Islam.

The Critical Battle of Badr

At the wells of Badr, near the coast of the Red Sea, Muhammad's 300-man army was caught off guard by a superior force from Mecca. Although outnumbered 3-to-1, the Muslims defeated the Meccans.

Mohammad claimed his victory had been due to thousands of angels, led by Jabril (Gabriel), who had fought for them.

This battle was significant because if Mohammad's army had lost, or if Mohammad had been killed, it would have been the end of the Muslim movement. The victory gained converts as well as prestige among Arabs and other people of the region.

'The Quraysh Model' of Meccan Conquest

Three years after the Battle of Badr, a 10,000-man Meccan army again laid siege to Medina. The Quraysh tribe of Mecca was not able to conquer Medina, and Mohammad was not strong enough to defeat them. So Mohammad signed a ten-year treaty of non-aggression with Mecca.

By A.D. 630, less than a year later, Mohammad had built up his army. He stormed Mecca by surprise and conquered it, thus making himself ruler of the city of his birth.

Mohammad's first act was to establish Mecca as the holiest city of Islam. John Noss records about that incident:

> One of his first acts was to go reverently to the Ka'ba; yet he showed no signs of yielding to the ancient Meccan polytheism. After honoring the Black Stone and riding seven times around the shrine, he ordered the destruction of the idols within it and sanctioned the use of the well Zamzam and restored the boundary pillars defining the sacred territory around Mecca.[11]

Mohammad proclaimed the Kabah as "Haram" (forbidden to non-Muslims). Islam now had two capitals—Medina the political, and Mecca the religious.

Muslims have quoted the "Quraysh Model" as justification for many deceptive treaties. It means, "Negotiate 'peace' with your enemy until you become strong enough to annihilate him." This is the justification Chairman Yasser Arafat gave to his critics who condemned him for signing the Oslo Agreement.

Why Jews Were Persecuted

Mohammad and his disciples treated the Jews more severely than any other "unbelievers." Why? "They had irritated him by their refusal to recognize him as a prophet, by ridicule and by argument," explains Guillaume. "And of course their economic supremacy was a standing irritant." Guillaume continues,

> Their leaders opposed his claim to be an apostle sent by God, and though they doubtless drew some satisfaction from his acceptance of the divine mission of Abraham,

---

11. John B. Noss, *Man's Religions*, (MacMillian Publishing Co. Inc., 1974), p. 517.

Moses and the prophets, they could hardly be expected to welcome the inclusion of Jesus and Ishmael among his chosen messengers.[12]

Mohammad decided these non-believers, these skeptics in his homeland, had to be eliminated if he was going to fulfill his imperial ambitions. So he ordered an Islamic law: "Two religions may not dwell together on the Arabian Peninsula."

The Arabian Holocaust

After issuing this decree, Mohammad wasted no time in enforcing it. He went after the Jewish communities of northern Arabia, systematically slaughtering them all. First, the Quraiza tribe was exterminated. Then Mohammad sent messengers to the Jewish community at the oasis of Khaibar, "inviting" Usayr, their war chief, to visit Medina for peace negotiations.

"Usayr set off with 30 companions and a Muslim escort," writes historian Norman Stillman. "Suspecting no foul play, the Jews went unarmed. On the way the Muslims turned upon the defenseless delegation, killing all but one who managed to escape."[13] Mohammad attacked and destroyed their whole community.

Mohammad justified this treachery saying, "War is deception." War practiced according to this Muslim doctrine was not just deception, it was like a literal hell—even with primitive weapons of the seventh century. The complete annihilation of the two Arabian-Jewish tribes, with every man, woman and child slaughtered, is, according to the late Israeli historian and President Itzhak Ben-Zvi, "a tragedy for which no parallel can be found in Jewish history."[14]

Parenthetically, in the current war against Islamic Fundamentalist terrorism, it would be good for Western leaders to remember

---

12. Guillaume, *Islam*, p. 43.

13. Norman Stillman, *The Jews of Arab Lands*, (Philadelphia, PA.: 1979), p. 17.

14. Peters, *From Time Immemorial*, p. 144.

this "Islamic tactic of warfare." According to this "religious" doc-trine of Islam, what they say does not have to be true—after all, "war is deception." And the end justifies the means.

A Heritage of Brutality

As an example of their brutality and barbarity, after one Jewish town surrendered to the Muslims, approximately 1000 men were be-headed in one day. The women and children were sold into slavery.[15]

Elsewhere, as the attacks on Jews continued, some managed to survive. Under a new Islamic policy, non-Muslims or "infidels" were permitted to maintain their land so long as they paid a 50 percent tribute for "protection."[16] Peters writes:

> Thus the Jewish *dhimmi* evolved—the robbery of free-dom and political independence compounding the extor-tion and eventual expropriation of property. Tolerated between onslaughts, expulsions and pillages from the Arab Muslim conquest onward, the non-Muslim dhimmi—predominantly Jewish but with Christians too—provided the important source of religious revenue through the "infidel's" head tax. He became very quickly a convenient political scapegoat and whipping boy as well."[17]

The 'Irresistible Appeal' of Islam

The Bedouin's were raised to fight, raid and pillage. It was endemic in their genes. As historian Philip Hitti wrote concern-ing them:

> The raid is raised by the economic and social conditions of desert life to the rank of a national institution. *It lies at the base of the economic structure of Bedouin pastoral society. In desert land, where the fighting mood is a chron-*

---

15. Guillaume, *Islam*, p. 47–48.

16. Ibid.

17. Ibid., emphasis added.

ic mental condition, raiding is one of the few manly occu-
pations. An early Arab poet gave expression to the guid-
ing principle of such life in two verses: "Our business is to
make raids on the enemy, on our neighbor and on our
own brother, in case we find none to raid but a brother!"[18]

Now Mohammad tells them they can fight, raid and pillage in
the sanctified service of Allah—and keep the booty as well. Fighting is now raised to the level of a "holy war" in the cause of Allah.
In fact, an old Arabic word is dusted off and given new meaning
—*"Jihad,* Holy War."

Guillaume explains how this new policy of repression and con-
fiscation led to Islam's growing appeal among the nomadic Arab
tribes:

> Much of the wealth of the country which had been con-
> centrated in the hands of the Jews had now been seized
> by the Muslims, who were no longer indigents but wealthy
> landowners, men of substance, owning camels and hors-
> es and their own weapons . . . Mohammad's fame
> spread far and wide, and the Bedouin flocked to him in
> thousands.[19]

The plunder of Jewish people directly led to explosive growth
and popularity of Islam among the Arabs is supported by Islamic
historian Ali Dashti who writes, "The immediate step which
secured the economic base and strengthened the prestige of the
Muslims was their seizure of the property of the Jews at Yathrib."[20]

The Precedent of Prey

The betrayal and killing of Jews at Medina, the massacres of
the Nadhir and Kainuka tribes and the dispossession of property
by Muslims set up what Joan Peters rightly calls "the precedent of

---

18. Philip Hitti, *The Arabs: A Short History,* (Washington DC: Regnery Publishing, Inc., 1996),
emphasis added, <http://www.oneworldmagazine.org/focus/deserts/toc.htm>.

19. Guillaume, *Islam,* pp. 49–50.

20. Ali Dashti, *23 Years: A Study of the Prophetic Career of Muhammad,* (London: George Allen &
Unwin, 1985), p. 86.

prey"—a pattern that would be repeated again and again. The agrarian and merchant Jews lucky enough to escape death would be plundered and exploited by nomadic Arabs. Islam not only gave them an excuse for such oppression, *it commanded it.*

It is likely that among Jewish refugees fleeing from Arabia were numbers of Jews whose "Palestinian"—or Judean—ancestors had fled from the Romans.

> Now they returned to seventh-century Palestine, joining their Jewish brethren who had never left. Ironically, the Jewish refugees return coincided with the introduction of the Arab conquerors from the desert; the very invaders who had forced themselves in and the Jews out of their homes in Arabia would now plunder Judah-Palestine in the identical pattern. And the Jews who inhabited many towns of "Palestine" uninterruptedly would one day in the twentieth century be forced out as the Arabian Jews had been —by slaughter or expropriation and terrorizing. The towns would then, in the later twentieth century, be touted as purely Arab Palestinian areas since time immemorial, just as the Arabian Peninsula had come to be perceived as "purely Arab," when in fact the holy Arab Muslim city of Medina had been originally settled by Jews.[21]

If you think over this correction of history, it is truly remarkable. Talk about myths. The Arab Muslims have spun the mother of all myths with their claim "Palestine has always been Arab— from time immemorial."

All over the world today—from Georgia to Azerbaijan to Serbia to India to Sudan and Eritrea—long-forgotten ethnic tensions resulting from historical injustices and frightening memories are on the rise. Is it any wonder, given the enormity of the atrocities against the Jews, that Israelis would be suspicious of experts who are quick to say, "The past is the past"? Former Israeli Prime Minister Benjamin Netanyahu has reason to say, "It isn't the size of Israel that bothers the Muslims; it is the existence of Israel."

---

21. Peters, *From Time Immemorial*, p. 145.

Until the past is fully explored in a truthful and open way, there is no hope of rectifying history's injustices. The "Medina Legacy" established a pattern of institutionalized Islamic anti-Semitism that is at the very root of today's Middle East crisis. Without addressing that reality, there is no hope of understanding, let alone settling, the conflict.

CHAPTER NINE

Institutionalized Anti-Semitism

"The Resurrection of the dead will not come until the Muslims will war with the Jews and the Muslims will kill them . . . the trees and rocks will say, 'O Muslim, here is a Jew behind me, come and kill him'"

THE PROPHET MOHAMMAD[1]

*"The power struggle between Israel and the Arabs is a long-term historical trial. Victory or defeat are for us questions of existence or annihilation, **the outcome of an irreconcilable hatred.**"*

AL RIYADH SAUD, FOUNDER OF THE KINGDOM OF SAUDI ARABIA
EMPHASIS ADDED

"The war is open until Israel ceases to exist and until the last Jew in the world is eliminated."

HAMAS LEADER[2]

---

1. From the Hadith, which records the acts and sayings of Mohammad.

2. *Wall Street Journal*, December 18, 1992.

Hate, a Religious Doctrine

What began as rivalry between brothers degenerated into a family feud. It evolved into an everlasting, irreconcilable hatred.

There were some cases of reconciliation between the Arabs and Jews of Arabia in the centuries before the birth of Mohammad. They were not loved, but they were accepted. Some Arabs who lived by Jewish communities even converted to Judaism.

Joan Peters notes concerning this period, "It was the Prophet Muhammad himself who attempted to negate the positive image of the Jew that had been prevalent earlier."[3]

Hatred of Jews in Islam is justified as a religious cause. Islam literally resurrected the ancient enmities and jealousies of the sons of Ishmael, Esau and Keturah toward Jews and enshrined them as religious doctrine.

Although this information may be a bit overloaded with facts, it is absolutely essential we understand it if we are to comprehend the doublespeak and outright myths that are being set forth by Muslims in negotiations with Western diplomats over Palestine.

Beginning with Mohammad and continuing to this day Islam contains an inherently anti-Jewish character. Despite tales to the contrary, this characteristic has meant centuries of horror for non-Muslims (especially Jews)—or dhimmis, as they are called—unfortunate enough to be forced to live in an Arab land. This anti-Jewish attitude of Islam has multiplied a hundred-fold since the birth of the modern Jewish State in 1948.

EXPONENTIAL SPREAD OF JEW-HATE

Before Mohammad and Islam, endemic hatred for Jews was largely confined to Arabs and the Arabian Peninsula. But since

---

3. Joan Peters, *From Time Immemorial* (New York, N.Y.: Harper & Row, 1984), p. 33.

loathing of Jews is enshrined in the Koran and traditions of Islam, wherever Islam has spread, Jew-hate has spread with it.

So today, Muslims in Indonesia are not Arabs, nor do they have much contact with Jews, nor a natural relationship to "Palestine." But they abhor Jews because it's part of their religion and faith.

The same can be said of the Muslims of Afghanistan, Pakistan, Chechnya, etc. They are not Arab, but they've caught their hatred of the Jew like a incredibly contagious disease.

Deification of 7th Century Arab Culture

The Muslim religion actually froze in time the seventh century Arab culture of Mecca and raised it to the level of being a "Divine Revelation"—how all people should live for all time. The modern concept of "Jihad" primarily has to do with forcing this culture upon the whole world—either by conversion or conquest.

In a profound, almost mystical sense, Mohammad is the product of seventh century Arab culture, and the Muslim religion is an expression of his perceptions of it. A major part of this being a revulsion of the Jew. Mohammad never forgave them for rejecting him and his claim of being God's Prophet. Without question, that hostility was woven into the Koran.

A modern example of how profoundly Arab culture is part of Islam is provided by the return of the Ayatollah Khomeini to Iran in 1979. As soon as he took over, he ripped the people away from twentieth century advancements and dragged them back to seventh century Arab culture. Thousands who did not comply were executed. Others escaped with only the clothes on their backs. And as usual, the Jewish community that had settled there during the Shah's tolerant reign fled for their lives.

To the Muslim fundamentalist, Western culture is evil. Not because it is sinful in a moral sense, but because it is different from Arab ways. This is why they dispise democracy—there is no precedent for it in their culture nor in the Koran.

RELIGIOUS-CULTURAL IMPERIALISM

Islam is nothing less than a religious-cultural imperialism that works to take over the world. This is why Mohammad divided the earth into two spheres:

- Dar al-Islam—the land of peace

- Dar al-harb—the land of war.

Mohammad believed the Muslim is in a perpetual state of "Jihad"—"holy war"—with all countries in the Dar al-harb sphere. The true follower believes that Allah has willed for Muslims to establish Islamic ways over the whole world—either by conversion or sword.

Islam believes this doctrine is especially applicable to the Middle East, which they claim as the center of their world. They contend that any land captured and held by Muslim forces in the past is sacred. But their myths built around Jerusalem and Palestine make it second only to Mecca and Media as a most holy place.

A remnant of Jews has always continued to dwell in Jerusalem and Palestine in spite of the dangers and difficulties. But when Jews began to return in growing numbers at the end of the nineteenth century, it caused Muslims great alarm.

When the Jews declared soverignty in Palestine in 1948, it was considered "Al Nabka"—a catastrophe. Their continuing presence is viewed as the ultimate blasphemy to Islam, a desecration of the "Third Holiest Place in Islam," and an insult to Allah that must be cleansed.

Israel's victories over the "armies of Allah" in five wars have placed the Koran in jeopardy, for it promises the forces of Islam victory in "holy wars." Devout Muslims fervently believe this is something that must be rectified. Nothing can remove this insult to Allah but a final military defeat of Israel.

RELIGION, CULTURE AND LAND

Land is looked upon by Islam differently than by other religions. Once Islamic culture is established in an area, it is considered sanctified to Allah. It becomes "Dar al-Islam"—the land of peace. When an invader takes it away, Muslims are obligated to take it back for Allah, no matter what the sacrifice.

This is why Muslim forces fought European Crusaders for three centuries over "the Holy Land." But now the Jew has "invaded." Islamic's ancient enmity toward them has made this an intolerable insult. They point to Israel as "a cancer in the heart of Islam that must be removed."

Western civilization just does not understand this basic Islamic thinking. Western media particularly don't have a clue as to what motivates the Muslim—or what strategies he will use to fulfill his duty to Allah. This is why they swallow Muslim propaganda "hook, line and sinker." As we will see, the modern Arab myths spun about "legitimate rights of the Palestinian refugees" and "Israel's occupation of Palestinian territory" are based on monstrous distortions of history.

As Mohammad said, "War is deception." He set the example for negotiating peace with an enemy until you are strong enough to annihilate him. It is called "the Quraysh Model." This was the ten-year peace treaty Mohammad signed with the Quraysh tribe of Mecca, which within a year he broke by destroying them. This is how he conquered Mecca and made it the holiest site in Islam—through treachery.

Rise Of The 'Khaliph Rasul Allahs'

Mohammad's death in A.D. 632 was unexpected and sudden, leaving Islam with no plan of succession. The fact that Mohammad had no male heir made the problem much more difficult. This left problems that resulted in major conflicts within the Muslim religion.

It is not my purpose to trace every detail of this phase of Islam.

But it did result in the formation of the Shi'ite and Sunni sects.

Basically, the Shi'ites believed the "Khaliph Rasul Allah" or the *Successor of the Messenger of God,* had to be in the bloodline of Mohammad. The Sunni sect, however, held the majority opinion. They believed any worthy member of the faithful was eligible to succeed Mohammad, though some added it was preferable he should be of the Quraysh tribe.

THE FIRST OF 'THE DIVINELY GUIDED ONES'

Mohammad's first four successors, or Khaliphs, are known collectively as the "rashidun", or the *Divinely Guided Ones.* They each knew the Prophet personally and worked with him to build and spread Islam. Thus, their credentials were as unique as their thirty years of rule (A.D. 632–662). Their accomplishments were nothing short of extraordinary.

After some controversy, Abu Bakr Sedeik (A.D. 632–634) became the first to possess the title of *Khaliph Rasul Allah.* This reflected the temporal authority of the Prophet and his responsibility as defender of the faithful. Since Mohammad was "the last, or Seal of the Prophets," the Khaliph was not the spiritual head of the House of Islam but the secular "Commander of the Faithful."

Bakr's khaliphate magnified, if not created, a schism that endures to this day via the geo-religio-politcal division of the Shi'ite and Sunni sects.

When the Shi'ites' choice, Ali, was not chosen as Khaliph, a violent struggle erupted that continues until today. Ali ibn Talib was not only Mohammad's first cousin and adopted son, but he married Mohammad's only surviving child, his daughter Fatima. If you think that this is irrelevant, remember that Sunni Iraq fought a bloody war with Shi'ite Iran over this issue the entire decade of the 1980's.

In the Muslim Middle East, events that happened centuries ago can be as relevant as those that happened yesterday. A grudge based on an event that occurred a thousand years ago can erupt today into a savage war against the "descendants of the offender."

Only two issues in history have united the Sunnis and the Shi'ites. The first was the long war against Christian Crusaders in the Middle Ages, and the second is their mutual hatred and destructive desire for the State of Israel. It's truly amazing, but after Iraq and Iran inflicted over a million casualties on each other, they are now "kissing and making up" because of Israel.

Bakr's short two-year khaliphate was spent re-uniting the tribes of Arabia, most of which had immediately revolted after Moham-mad's death. He was helped by an amazing military leader named Khalid ibn-Walid, who became known as "the Sword of Allah."[4]

OMAR, 'THE SECOND FOUNDER OF ISLAM'

Omar ibn al-Khattab, by prearrangement, succeeded Bakr and reigned from A.D. 634–644. He is important to know because he devastated the Christian world with a vengeance.

> Historian George Grant gave this description of Omar:
> A stern giant of a man with a long dark beard and a full, brooding countenance. He wore coarse, frayed garments and always carried a whip in his right fist in order to en-force righteous humility among his men. He had little appreciation for the accomplishments of Byzantine and was single-minded in his desire to bring the empire to its knees.[5]
>
> . . . According to the *Sah Nemeh*, a contemporary chron-icle of caliphs and kings, Omar despised the Christian infi-dels for their "half-faith" and yearned to force their confessions, creeds, and liturgies into extinction . . .[6]

Omar was driven as one empowered by "a supernatural spirit,"

---

4. Tom Fontanes, *Islam, A History* (Special Report for *Countdown Magazine*: October, 1991). To my knowledge, the full report was never published, but I express my gratitude for many valuable insights obtained from this work.

5. George Grant, *Blood Of The Moon* (Wolgemuth & Hyatt Publishers: 1991), p. 64.

6. Ibid.

which probably explains his amazing career. Under his "inspired leadership" the united tribes of Arabia exploded from the Peninsula. They charged in every direction, conquering and occupying all they encountered.

The exploits of Walid, "the Sword of Allah," are vital to this book. In A.D. 635, Walid entered the borders of Persia and subdued the village of Hira. He then made an incredible forced march across the Syrian Desert to join forces with another Muslim army near Jerusalem. In short order, out numbered two-to-one, Walid led his forces in a series of brilliant cavalry charges that cut the Byzantine defenders to pieces.

Walid quickly conquered the territory known as Palestine. By the fall, Walid reached the gates of Damascus, having decimated the opposition along the way. After a six-month siege, the Muslims captured the ancient city.

JERUSALEM'S FIRST FALL TO ISLAM

In the fateful month of August, A.D. 635, the Muslim armies captured Jerusalem.

Khaliph Omar arived in February of A.D. 638 and personally proclaimed the Temple Mount one of Islam's holiest sites. He built a wooden Mosque over the great rock they believed to be the site where Abraham built an alter to sacrifice Isaac; where David built an altar to quell God's discipline of Israel; and where Solomon placed the Ark of the Covenant. I personally believe they picked the wrong rock, but that is an issue for another book.

Muslims developed the legend that this rock is the foundation stone from which Allah created the earth and the place where Adam made atonement after his fall. Even more significant, the Muslims believe Mohammad ascended to heaven from there on a horse that sprouted wings. This is the basis of designating it the third holiest site of Islam.

Chuck Missler quotes Steve Runciman concerning Omar's triumphant entry to Jerusalem,

> On a February day in the year A.D. 638 the Khaliph Omar entered Jerusalem, riding upon a white camel. He was dressed in worn filthy robes, and the army that followed him was rough and unkempt; but its discipline was perfect . . . Omar rode straight to the sight of the Temple of Solomon . . . Omar was shocked at the filth and rubble that lay strewn about the Temple Mount. Because the holy sight had been neglected he made the Christian Patriarch (Sophronius) grovel in the muck. Afterward Omar set about clearing the sight. He then built a wooden mosque on the temple mount.[7]

OMAR'S AMAZING CONQUESTS

During the nine years of Omar's khaliphate, Muslims grew from a regional kingdom on the Arabian Peninsula to become an Islamic World-Empire. Grant comments on this amazing feat:

> Before his death in A.D. 644 (Omar) had spread the dominion of Islam from the Euphrates across the North African Littoral. He had conquered all of Iraq, brought Persia to the brink of collapse, controlled the southern Mediterranean coastline, and put Christendom on the defensive at every turn. In addition, he left his successors a tumultuous momentum that gave them expansive new conquests in Spain, Sicily, Crete, and Italy.[8]

Essential to our focus, Omar's conquests brought Jewish communities, which lived in the areas for hundreds of years, under his brutal control. Those not killed received the status of something only slightly less terrible—they became "dhimmis," a word for non-Muslims living under Muslim rule.

Most of the Christian Byzantine civilization was also conquered and survivors suffered a similar fate. Historic churches were converted to Mosques. Priceless Christian art was obliterated. Every-

---

7. Chuck Missler & Don Stewart, *The Coming Temple* (Dart Press: 1991), p. 65.

8. Grant, *Blood Of The Moon*, p. 59.

thing Christian was destroyed. Whatever referred to Jesus as the Son of God was removed. In its place, Muslims posted ornate signs that read, "All praise be to Allah who never had a son."

ISLAM'S 'BENEVOLENT LAW' FOR 'DHIMMIS'

It was under Khaliph Omar that Muslim laws regarding non-believers were firmly established. As dhimmis, Jews were forbidden to touch the Koran, forced to wear distinctive clothes and a yellow badge (Christians had to wear blue). They were not permitted to perform religious practices in public, not allowed to own or ride a horse, and not authorized to show any public expression of grief when they buried their dead.

As an expression of gratitude for being allowed to live among Muslims, dhimmis were expected to pay special confiscatory taxes prescribed by the Koran—at least 50 percent of all earnings.

Here is an example of "Islamic justice" for the Jewish dhimmis:

> Islamic religious law decreed that, although the murder of one Muslim by another Muslim was punishable by death, a Muslim who murdered a non-Muslim was not given the death penalty, but only the obligation to pay "blood money" to the family of the slain infidel. Even this punishment was unlikely, however, because the law held the testimony of a Jew or a Christian invalid against a Muslim, and the penalty could only be exacted under improbable conditions—when two Muslims were willing to testify against a brother Muslim for the sake of an infidel.[9]

This kind of blatantly ruthless double-standard has continued through the centuries—enforced to varying degrees of cruelty depending on the character of the Muslim ruler and country. Under the best circumstances, life was merely intolerable and filled with indignities. *In the worst of circumstances, Jews and Christians lived every moment of every day in fear for their lives.*

---

9. Peters, *From Time Immemorial*, p.34.

Jews dwelling in Muslim lands lived under the terrible law of the dhimmi. As Islam spread, Jewish communities were swept into the storm. Those who weren't killed lived in humiliation and terror.

What Moses predicted centuries before about the Israelites became a grim reality:

> **Moreover, the LORD will scatter you among all peoples, from one end of the earth to the other end of the earth . . . And among those nations you shall find no rest, and there shall be no resting place for the sole of your foot; but there the LORD will give you a trembling heart, failing of eyes, and despair of soul. So your life shall hang in doubt before you; and you shall be in dread night and day, and shall have no assurance of your life.**[10]

True, Jews were persecuted in other cultures as well, but the Muslims made it a religious sacrament.

Slavery and Dehumanization

The practices of slavery and dehumanization of the Jews continue to the present day. Here are a few examples of ancient Jewish communities, and how they have carried on to our present era.

YEMEN

Life for Jews in Yemen has always been particularly demeaning. For example, Jews were treated like subhuman slaves, forced to clean the public latrines and clear the streets of animal carcasses without pay on the Sabbath day.[11]

A particularly heartless Yemenite law decreed fatherless Jewish children under 13 be taken from their mothers and raised Muslim. According to historian Goitein:

> Children were torn away from their mothers. To my mind this law, which was enforced with new vigor about 50

---

10. Deuteronomy 28:64–66.

11. Peters, *From Time Immemorial*, p. 34.

years ago, more than anything else impelled the Yemenite Jews to quit that country to which they were very much attached. The result was that many families arrived in Israel with one or more of their children lost to them . . . some widows were bereaved in this way of all their offspring.[12]

Persecution in Yemen was consistent and extreme. Stoning Jews continued as an age-old custom until most Yemenite Jews left for Israel in 1948. They had lived in Yemen for 2500 years.

BABYLON/IRAQ

Jews had a long history of residence in Babylon until the Muslim conquest in A.D. 634. Later, heavy taxes were imposed, synagogues razed and ultimately, entire communities slaughtered.

In the modern era, after Israel became a state, the Iraqis came down on them with pent up fury. There had been persecution in the region, but this was appalling. More than 123,000 Iraqi Jews fled to Israel in terror between 1949 and 1952 alone. Many were killed in riots. Those who fled left with nothing but the clothes on their backs, thankful they escaped with their lives. They left behind the wealth and property their families accumulated over some 2500 years. Most of these families could trace their Iraq origins back to Babylonian captivity in the days of Daniel the Prophet.

EGYPT

Prior to 1948, the Jewish community in Egypt lived in relative peace and harmony compared to the plight of Jews in neighboring Muslim nations. Their lives, however, were filled with constant uncertainty. Humiliations, property confiscations and physical atrocities happened daily at the whim of Muslim neighbors.

Beginning in 1940, spurred by Nazi propaganda and the growth of the Zionist movement, many Jews were killed in anti-Jewish riots. Egypt passed laws that all but prohibited Jews from being

---

12. Ibid., p. 38.

employed. The government confiscated property, and after the 1947 vote to partition Palestine, Jewish homes were looted and synagogues destroyed.

In one 10-day period in 1948, 150 Jews were murdered or seriously wounded in Egyptian bloodletting. In 1949, as soon as a ban was lifted on Jews leaving the country, 20,000 fled Egypt, mostly for Israel, with no thought to packing their belongings.

ADMIRATION FOR HITLER

Egypt's Gamal Abdel Nasser openly declared in 1964, "Our sympathy was with the Germans. The president of our Parliament, for instance, Anwar Sadat, was imprisoned for his sympathy with the Germans."[13]

In the 1970s, a prominent Egyptian writer was, once more, helping to stir up the old blood libels against Jews. Anis Mansour assured his readers the medieval lie that Jews sacrificed children and drank their blood was historically true and that "the Jews confessed." Because of this, he said it was perfectly appropriate to persecute "the wild beasts." Another time he wrote:

> People all over the world have come to realize that Hitler was right, since Jews . . . bloodsuckers . . . interested in destroying the whole world which has . . . expelled them and despised them for centuries . . . and burnt them in Hitler's crematoria . . . one million . . . six million—I would that he had finished it![14]

Mansour is hardly regarded as a renegade in Egypt. In 1975, he represented the nation at the 40th International PEN (writers') Conference in Vienna. On his return, he charged that "the Jews are guilty" for Nazism, and they "have only themselves to blame."[15]

---

13. Ibid., p. 36.

14. Ibid., p. 37. Peters quotes Mansour from the Arab newspaper *Al-Akhbar*, August 19, 1973.

15. Ibid.

SYRIA

Egypt was a walk in the park compared to Syria. It was a living hell for Jews. The smoldering hatred for them that has always been in Syria burst into a roaring fire with the advent of Zionism. Damascus became the headquarters of anti-Jewish activities and feasted on Nazism.

During World War II, the Jewish quarter was raided several times because of ridiculous rumors that Churchill and Roosevelt agreed to make Syria into a Jewish state.

Israelis have told me on many occasions that the most vicious enemy in the whole Middle Eastern neighborhood is Syria—a rough neighborhood. Today, Damascus is host to offices of virtually every Islamic terror organization on the planet.

JEW-HATING TAUGHT FROM INFANCY

Not only do Muslim families teach their children to hate Jews from the cradle, but they also interweave this message of genocide into their textbooks.

Today, Muslim governments have official policies against Jews written into public schoolbooks. For example:

- "The Jews in Europe were persecuted and despised because of their corruption, meanness and treachery." Found in Jordanian history textbooks from 1966 onward.

- "Israel was born to die. Prove it." Instructions in a Jordan High School.

- "The Jews . . . live exiled and despised since by their nature they are vile, greedy and enemies of mankind." Syrian junior high school textbook.

- "We shall expel all the Jews from Muslim lands." A fifth year elementary school syntax exercise in a Syrian textbook.

- "The Arabs do not cease to act for the extermination of Israel." An Egyptian junior high school grammar exercise.

- "Israel hopes to be the homeland of the Jew, and they have the stubbornness of 4,000 years of history behind them. But Israel shall not live if the Arabs stand fast in their hatred. She shall wither and decline. Even if all the human race, and the devil in Hell, conspire to aid her, she shall not exist," said an Egyptian ninth-grade text.

OFFICIAL ANTI-JEWISHNESS

Peters writes:

> The anti-Semitic literature published by the Arabs since World War II has been voluminous, and is continually increasing, despite the almost total evacuation of the Arab world's Jews. The virulence of this literature is disturbing, but even more significant is the official or governmental origin of the publications—not from an extremist fringe, which might be lightly dismissed, but from Arab governments, including those called "moderate." [16]

El-Ahram, the leading daily with over 700,000 readers, carried a book review of "The First Terrorists," in which the critic, Abd El-Muneim Qandil, asserted March 3, 1987:

> I lower my pen in respect to the author who presents proof from Israeli books to the malice of the Jews who wish to kill all male newborns and pregnant women in order to uproot the Palestinians. . . . The author speaks about turning facts upside down . . . such as their claim that the gas chambers used by Hitler to get rid of people infected by plague were especially built to burn Jews alive.

El Masa, a daily of 100,000, reported April 21, 1987:

> Jews distributed a "ridiculous lie" after the Second World War concerning the Holocaust. They started with the claim that 100,000 Jews were exterminated but later

---

16. Ibid., p. 39.

reached the figure of 8 million. Jews are inflating these numbers in order to achieve bigger help from the USA. . . . We can expect, therefore, that very soon the number of Jews killed by the Nazis will reach 10 million.

Sawt El-Arab, a daily with a circulation of 100,000, stated on March 15, 1987:

Israel sells to Egypt seeds, plants and cattle infected with diseases in order to destroy the local agriculture.

El Mukhtar El-Islami, a Monthly religious publication, claimed in April of 1986:

The Jews were responsible for World War II. They initiated this war in order to crush Nazi Germany, which was the last obstacle before Jewish domination of the world. Europe was indeed destroyed and Zionist strategy had its victory. The Jews were also behind the murder of President Abraham Lincoln.

El-Nur, a weekly publication of the Muslim Brotherhood, circulation over 100,000, said October 22, 1986:

We wait for the moment that all Jews will gather in Palestine and that will be the great day for enormous massacre.

Sawt Filastin, a semi-official weekly published for Palestinians in August, 1987, the fifth anniversary of the Sabra and Shatilla massacre, said:

Deception and treason are basic components of Jewish character. Jews always used tricks and plots to spread terror and death all over the world.

El-Tawhid, a fundamentalist Islamic monthly, stated in February 1987:

The children of Israel are "garbage allied with Satan, purulence causing pain and infection, a deposit of germs."

Many more examples could be quoted here, but these illustrate the irrational hatred constantly spread against the Jew in the Muslim world. And it is getting worse by the day.

Christians Also Increasingly Targeted

Assaults on Christians are growing as illustrated by the 9/11 attack on the USA. Islamic fundamentalists see the USA as the center of the Judeo-Christian based world order, which they believe is the greatest threat to true Islam. They believe we must be destroyed and replaced with an Islamic based world order.

Just as the Jews were driven out of Muslim lands, Christians are the newest targets. Here are a few examples of the kind of persecution occurring throughout the Islamic world.

- Indonesia, which has the largest Muslim population of any country in the world, is systematically killing and terrorizing Christians. More than 500 Churches have been burned and hundreds of Christians killed. Others have fled in fear for their lives.

- Muslims of the Sudan have been systematically slaughtering Christians in Eritrea and Ethiopia. Thousands have been killed, millions have been driven into exile resulting in tens of thousands dying of famine.

- In Egypt, Muslim fundamentalists have forced Christians to stay inside their mud hovels for months due to the intensity of persecution. Churches have been burned, Christian shops looted and destroyed and some have been killed. One Coptic Christian said, "Life for Christians is over. Now we must figure out how to get out alive." Coptic Christians, who number seven to eight million of Egypt's 56 million people, belong to one of the oldest denominations in Christendom.[17]

Because the "Christian US soldiers" have stayed in Saudi Arabia to defend it against Iraqi invasion, Osama Bin-Laden has interpreted this as ultimate sacrilege. To him and his Al Qaida, our mere presence on Saudi soil constitutes an invasion of sacred Islamic land and desecrates the most holy places of Islam.

---

17. *New York Times*, July 27, 1992.

Listen to part of Bin-Laden's "Fatwa", which declared a "Jihad" against all Americans,

> For over seven years the United States has been occupying the lands of Islam in the holiest of places, the Arabian Peninsula, plundering its riches, dictating to its rulers, humiliating its people, terrorizing its neighbors, and turning its bases in the Peninsula into a spearhead through which to fight the neighboring Muslim peoples. . . .

For this and equally "serious crimes", Osama concludes,

> We—with God's help—call on every Muslim who believes in God and wishes to be rewarded to comply with God's order to KILL THE AMERICANS and plunder their money whenever and wherever they find it. We call on Muslim ulema, leaders, youths, and soldiers to launch the raid on Satan's U.S. troops and the devil's supporters allying with them, and to displace those who are behind them so that they may learn a lesson.[18]

THE KORANIC VERSES

Like most westerners, you must be asking, "Where does this kind of hate come from"? We have seen how the animus started in the tents of Abraham and grew in the deserts of Arabia. But the constantly flowing spring that feeds and nourishes this hate is the Koran itself. The Muslim holy book pulls no punches in its denunciations of Jews, Christians and their faiths. I will close with a few examples. Later we will examine this issue in more detail. (All of the following verses were taken from an English translation on the Islamic website at http://hti.umich.edu/k/koran/browse.html).

> Certainly you will find the most violent of people in enmity for those who believe to be the Jews and those who are polytheists . . . (Surah 5.82)

> So when the sacred months have passed away, then slay the idolaters wherever you find them, and take them cap-

---

18. Adam Parfrey, *EXTREME ISLAM: Anti-American Propaganda of Muslim Fundamentalism* (Los Angeles,CA.: Feral House, 2001), pp. 291–292, emphasis added.

tives and besiege them and lie in wait for them in every ambush . . . (Surah 9.5)

O you who believe! Do not take the Jews and the Christians for friends; they are friends of each other; and whoever amongst you takes them for a friend, then surely he is one of them; surely Allah does not guide the unjust people. (Surah 5.51)

Abasement is made to cleave to them (Jews) wherever they are found, . . . and they have become deserving of wrath from Allah, and humiliation is made to cleave to them; this is because they disbelieved in the communications of Allah and slew the prophets unjustly; this is because they disobeyed and exceeded the limits. (Surah 3.112)

And you will most certainly find them (Jews) the greediest of men . . . (Surah 2.96)

And when there came to them (Jews) a Book from Allah (Koran) verifying that which they have . . . they disbelieved in him; so Allah's curse is on the unbelievers. Evil is that for which they (Jews) have sold their souls—that they should deny what Allah has revealed, out of envy that Allah should send down of His grace on whomsoever of His servants He pleases; so they have made themselves deserving of wrath upon wrath . . . (Surah 2.89 – 90)

Those who disbelieve in Our communications, We shall make them enter fire; so oft as their skins are thoroughly burned. We will change them for other skins, that they may taste the chastisement; surely Allah is Mighty, Wise. (Surah 4.56)

Of those who are Jews (they are those who) alter words from their places and say: We have heard and we disobey . . . but Allah has cursed them on account of their unbelief . . . (Surah 4:46)

Shall I inform you of him who is worse than this in the retribution from Allah? Worse is he (Jews) whom Allah has cursed and brought His wrath upon, and of *whom He made apes and pigs,* and he who served the *Satan*; these

are worse in place and more erring from the straight path.
(Surah 5.60, emphasis added)

With this kind of institutionalized anti-Semitism justified by their sacred book, their religious traditions and the example of Mohammad himself, is it any wonder that nearly all Jews living under Muslim rule gladly fled and left their possessions behind?

And is it any wonder that today's leaders of Israel are not anxious to rush into granting statehood to the Palestinians that would make their borders indefensible? Especially since they cannot stop the vicious terrorist attacks for even a week. Israel is being asked to give irreplaceable land and defensive positions for nothing more than the Muslim's promises of peace.

Maybe Israel's leaders have come to believe the Prophet Mohammad's words, "War is deception. Negotiate peace with your enemy until you are strong enough to annihilate him."

CHAPTER TEN

The Other Palestinian Refugees

"Over the last 40 years, the countries of the Middle East and North Africa have undergone radical transformations which, among other things, have brought about the near extinction of Jewish communities after 2,000 to 3,000 years of existence."

HISTORIAN/AUTHOR BAT YE'OR IN 1985

"The Jews always did live previously in Arab countries with complete freedom and liberty, as natives of the country. In fact, Muslim rule has always been tolerant . . . according to history Jews had a most quiet and peaceful residence under Arab rule."

HAJ AMIN AL-HUSSEINI, 1937—GRAND MUFTI JERUSALEM

The Untold Refugee Story

I f you read about the Middle East problem in the newspaper or listen to the discussions on the news, you can't help but be bombarded by analysts suggesting the key to peace is resolving "the Palestinian refugee issue." Well, prepare to be shocked. There is another virtually untold side of the Middle East refugee story.

Joan Peters put it so well in her monumental work, *From Time Immemorial:*

> For every refugee—adult or child—in Syria, Lebanon or elsewhere in the Arab world who compels our sympathy, there is a Jewish refugee who fled from the Arab country of his birth. For every Arab who moved to neighboring lands, a Jew was forced to flee from a community where he and his ancestors may have lived for 2,000 years.[1]

The world seldom, if ever, hears about the more than 800,000 Jewish refugees who fled Arab terror and hatred and settled in Israel. Perhaps it is because every single one of those refugees was accepted, resettled and provided for by the struggling Jewish state without question or hesitation. There never has been a Jewish refugee camp in Israel or anywhere else.[2]

EXODUS, PHASE II

Here are some indisputable facts. In 1948, there were more than 850,000 Jews living in the Arab world. Today, there are fewer than 29,000. Where were those Jewish dhimmi communities in the Arab world? Before Israel was reborn, between 125,00 and 135,000 Jews lived in Iraq; 75,000 lived in Egypt; 30,000 lived in Syria; 55,000 lived in Yemen; 8,000 lived in Aden; 265,000 lived in Morocco; up to 140,000 lived in Algeria; 105,000 lived in Tunisia; 5,000 lived in Lebanon; and some 38,000 lived in Libya.[3]

---

1. Joan Peters, *From Time Immemorial*, (New York, Harper & Row: 1984), p. 25.

2. *Facts and Logic About the Middle East Report*, San Francisco, 1992.

3. Peters, *From Time Immemorial*, p. 116.

Where are these Jews now? What happened to them? Where are their property and financial resources? Why are they never mentioned in the "Palestinian refugee debate" that keeps being trumpeted in the United Nations and the Media?

In her book, *From Time Immemorial*, Peters explains:

> The Arab world has been virtually emptied of its Jews, and the fledgling Jewish state would bear the burden of its hundreds of thousands of Jewish Arab-born refugees almost in secret. So unknown and undisclosed are these Arab-born Jews and the plight they have faced—the camps, squalor, uprooting, loss of property and security, discontent, unemployment and what they sensed to be neglect of their problems in Israel—that in countless conversations outside the Middle East with academics or professionals, from university graduates to blue-collar worker, including Jews as well as non-Jews, when the question of the "Middle East refugees" is raised, almost without exception the response is, "You mean the Palestinians—the Arabs, of course." It is as though the sad and painful story of the Arab-born Jewish refugees had been erased, their struggle covered over by a revision of the pages of history.[4]

WHY THE COVER UP?

Why isn't this story reported? Why isn't it chronicled? Why isn't it remembered? If Arab nations are responsible for expelling Jews in the same numbers as the much-publicized Arab refugees displaced after the creation of Israel, why isn't the obvious solution a simple population exchange? The enormity of the Muslim myth being swallowed by the West is nowhere more graphically illustrated than in this issue.

There is no moral equivalence in this situation.

The Jews did not drive out Palestinian refugees. They were not threatened or killed so as to terrorize survivors into leaving. In

---

4. Ibid., p. 71.

many cases Palestinians were begged to stay. However, they were ordered to leave "temporarily" by the combined Muslim armies who promised to annihilate Jews and the new state.

On the other hand, Jews living in Arab countries were terrorized, murdered and driven out. Their properties and assets were confiscated. Those who escaped were thankful just to be alive.

The Jews were received and immediately repatriated into the new fragile State of Israel. They were given aid and jobs to the best ability of the struggling new country.

The Palestinians were deliberately forced into refugee camps and not permitted to integrate into the society of their unwilling hosts —even though they were fellow Muslims. They didn't even try to help them; instead, they prevailed upon the United Nations to supply the refugees' needs. Kept in these camps by their own people for more than fifty years, they are used as political pawns so Muslim negotiators can continue to trump up charges of "Israeli aggression."

SOME POPULAR MUSLIM MYTHOLOGY

Many myths have been spun to suppress the facts about Jewish immigration from Arab lands. Some of these have been explored in earlier chapters. But let us review some of the tales that teach the exact opposite of the demonstrable truth:

- *Myth #1*: The Arabs have nothing against Jews in general and "lived in peace and harmony with them" until the creation of the Zionist Movement and consequent creation of the state of Israel in 1948.

- *Myth #2*: Alienation of Jews *began* in large part because Israel is almost entirely made up of European Jews who displaced indigenous Arab peoples in Palestine.

- *Myth #3*: The key to resolving the Middle East crisis is to stop "Israeli aggression and occupation of Arab lands" and to create an independent Palestinian state.

- *Myth #4:* Israel's U.S.-supplied military juggernaut has practiced continuous aggression against neighboring, peaceful Muslim nations who are only trying to right a terrible wrong forced upon them by the West.

These myths have worked like magic for Muslim propagandists for decades, but especially in present negotiations taking place since the Al Aqsa Intifada began in the fall of 2000.

You hear the propaganda "hot button" being pushed constantly —"Israeli aggression and occupation of Arab land." But in fact, as the world wrings its hands in distress over the so-called Palestinian refugee problem, one of the great untold stories of our age is that half of the Jewish population of Israel are refugees or offspring of refugees from Arab countries!

THE TERROR OF A DHIMMI'S LIFE

While there has been much misinformation about how Arab refugees in the Middle East became displaced, there is little doubt why Jews in Arab nations left their homes and belongings to flee for freedom and security in Israel. For anyone who makes the effort to investigate, the facts of history are easy to find.

"Clearly," writes Joan Peters, "the massive exodus of Jewish refugees from the Arab countries was triggered largely by the Arabs' own Nazi-like bursts of brutality, which had become the lot of the Jewish communities."[5]

Quite openly, Egypt's delegate to the United Nations General Assembly threatened the lives of Arab Jews in the 1947 debates over the rebirth of Israel: "The lives of one million Jews in Muslim countries would be jeopardized by partition," he blatantly warned.[6]

In reality, even the small handful of Jews still living in Arab lands do not remain by choice. In terms of percentage of popula-

---

5. Ibid., p. 80.

6. Mitchel G. Bard & Joel Himmelfarb, *Myths and Facts: A Concise Record of the Arab-Israeli Conflict,* (Near East Reports, Washington: 1992), p. 120.

tion and in real numbers, fewer Jews have chosen to live in Arab nations than those who chose to live in Hitler's Germany from 1933 to 1939.[7]

Why the contrast? Why did Jews forsake everything to leave Arab lands between 1948 and the present, while two-thirds of Germany's Jews, despite official anti-Semitic policies, stuck it out?

> Arab-born Jews realized that the Arab threats would be carried out, because they had lived as second-class— dhimmis—with reminders of pogroms in their own or their families' past experiences, whereas the German Jews felt themselves "assimilated," part of the German mainstream. They expressed initial "disbelief" that any such bigotry as the Nazis' could be more than a cruel political joke.[8]

No such illusions, however, were held with regard to the Arabs.

The big difference between 1930s Germany and the situation beginning in 1948 was that Jews now had a place to go—Israel.

Imagine you're a Jew living in an Arab land and you hear the following report on the radio:

> The Jews in the Arab countries have not respected the defense that Islam has given them for generations. They have encouraged World Zionism and Israel in every way in its aggression against the Arabs. . . . The Congress hereby declares that the Jews in the Muslim countries whose ties with Zionism and Israel are proved shall be regarded as fighters against the Muslims, unfit for the patronage and protection which the Muslim faith prescribes for adherents of peaceful protected faiths.

If you lived within range of Radio Amman in 1967, you would not have imagined such a broadcast. This was an actual report and typical of many others heard on Arab radio and television throughout the Middle East.[9]

---

7. Ibid., p. 133.

8. Peters, *From Time Immemorial*, p. 82.

9. Ibid., p. 78.

Arab propagandists and sympathizers have persisted in the charge that Israel is a foreign outpost of Western civilization, the intruding offspring of Europe inhabited by European survivors of Nazi brutality. In actuality, more than half of the people in Israel today are Jews or offspring of Jews who lived in Arab countries and have fled from Arab brutality; Israel's present population consists mainly of refugees and their descendants from two oppressions, European-Nazis and Arab.[10]

'COLLECTIVE AMNESIA'

For some reason, the whole world has swallowed unbelievable products of the Arab propaganda machine. As Egyptian author Bat Ye'or sees it, "even in Israel there is a kind of 'collective amnesia' with regard to the awesome contribution played by the Arab Jew in the history of the Jewish state."[11]

> The fact that the Zionist struggle was active mainly in Europe and America, and the fact that ignorance has prevailed concerning the dhimmi condition and its after-effects (insecurity, fear and silence), have led to Zionism's being viewed as an exclusively Western movement.

> The constant obfuscation of the Oriental dimension of Zionism has helped to foster the image of Israel as a colonial state of Western origin—even perceived as a reaction to Nazism. In this way Israel is defined within an exclusively Western framework, in contradiction to the realities of history, geography and its demography. Without in any way denying the specific dynamics of European Zionism and its essential achievements, nothing can change the fact that the fate of Palestine and its Jewish population was determined by the laws of jihad and its ulterior consequences. It is the historical amnesia specific to Oriental Jewry that has caused Zionism to be interpreted as an exclusively European movement, even though it is the stream in which all the currents of a nation, dismembered

---

10. Ibid., p. 79.

11. Bat Ye'or, *The Dhimmi*, (New Jersey, Fairleigh Dickinson University Press: 1985), p. 146.

by exile, converge and unite. This shortcoming is in part responsible for the difficulty of dialogue with those who attribute the present situation of the Palestinian Arab refugees to European colonialism and Nazism, whereas it is the consequence of a much more ancient tragedy. Only when the history of the dhimmis will have been taken into consideration will solutions be found to satisfy the rights of each party in conformity with historical realities.[12]

AN INCREDIBLE IRONY

Modern Media invented a perfect term for what Muslim nations have done with the history of "Dhimmis"—turnspeak—which means, "a cynical inverting or distorting of facts, which for example, makes the victim appear to be the oppressor." Arab propagandists have used turnspeak perfectly in perpetuating the myth of "displaced" and "terrorized" Arabs in the Jewish settled area of Palestine-cum-Israel.

The record shows the migrant Muslims came from other Arab lands to areas of Palestine that were reclaimed and developed by Jews in order to get jobs. It was afterward that they began to claim Jews displaced them from land that had been in their families for hundreds of years.

There have been colossal injustices inflicted on the people of Palestine—only it wasn't Jews who committed the injustices, but Muslims—who sought to drive Jews out of a plot of land that was only a fraction of what was originally mandated to them by the League of Nations. As we will see, when the map of the Middle East was completely redrawn after the fall of the Turkish Ottoman Empire in 1917, Arab states were created from the stateless remains of the Ottoman occupation, and a certain section was mandated to the Jews as a homeland. I hope everyone reading this book will clearly see that no matter how small the Jewish state was made, it was still too big for Muslims—because it isn't the size of Israel that matters to Muslims, it is the existence of Israel.

12. Ibid.

A RULE OF HATRED

The most cynical myth of all, however, is the lie that Jews enjoyed freedom, liberty and kind treatment while dwelling in Muslim ruled lands before the rise of Zionism. Here are some impartial observations of the Jews' or "Dhimmi's" treatment":

> In their Holy Land, the Jews as well as Christians, suffered long from harsh discrimination, persecution, and pogroms. According to the British Consulate report in 1839, *the Jew's life was not much above that of a dog.*

> In truth, *"Arab" terrorism in the Holy Land originated centuries before the recent tool of "the Palestinian cause was invented."* In towns where Jews lived for hundreds of years, those Jews were periodically robbed, raped, in some places massacred, and in many instances, the survivors were obliged to abandon their possessions and run.

> As we have seen, beginning with the Prophet Mohammad's edict demanding racial purity—that "Two religions may not dwell together . . ."—the Arab-Muslim world codified its supremacist credo, and later that belief was interpreted liberally enough to allow many non-Muslim dhimmis, or infidels, to remain alive between onslaughts in the Muslim world as a means of revenue. The infidel's head tax, in addition to other extortions—and the availability of the nonbelievers to act as helpless scapegoats for the oft-dissatisfied masses—became a highly useful mainstay to the Arab-Muslim rulers. Thus the pronouncement of the Prophet Mohammad was altered in practice to: two religions may not dwell together equally. That was the pragmatic interpretation.[13]

> In the early seventeenth century a pair of Christian visitors to Safed (Galilee) told of life for the Jews: "Life here is the poorest and most miserable that one can imagine." Because of the harshness of Turkish rule and its crippling dhimmi oppression, the Jews "pay for the very air they breathe."[14]

---

13. Peter's, *From Time Immemorial*, pp. 174–175, emphasis added.

14. John Hayman & Joseph von Egmont, *Travels* (London, 1759), cited by Katz in Battleground.

Reports like these could be multiplied. Shown to be a cynical lie is Haj Amin al-Husseini's claim that,

> The Jews always did live previously in Arab countries with complete freedom and liberty, as natives of the country. In fact, Muslim rule has always been tolerant . . . according to history Jews had a most quiet and peaceful residence under Arab rule.[15]

The audacity of this statement illustrates what Haj al-Husseini learned from his visit to Nazis Germany. Adolph Hitler, whom he greatly admired, developed the propaganda tactic of "the big lie."

One thing is certain, Jewish dhimmis were never treated with kindness, nor ever had anything approaching freedom. They were continually persecuted, brutalized and given degrading and humiliating treatment.

This monstrous myth, that there was no problem for the Jews living peacefully with the Muslims until the rise of Zionism and the founding of the state of Israel, is a classic example of Muslim "turnspeak" and the cynical hatred motivating it. The Muslim idea of humane, peaceful treatment for Jews is to have them subjected to the status of second rate citizens; to be available as taxable assets; to be scapegoats for whatever leadership failure or calamity that comes along; to be objects to hit, kick, rape, rob or murder whenever they need to let out aggression and frustration.

THE REAL REFUGEES

The Jews who lived in Muslim countries of the Middle East are in fact more truly refugees than the much-publicized "Palestinian refugees." It is supremely important to review the facts once more. Here are the contrasting conditions of how the two groups became "refugees."

The Palestinians were not driven out of Palestinian territory by Jewish threats and acts of terror. They left at the urging of fellow

---

15. Peters, *From Time Immemorial*, p. 172.

Muslims who promised it would only be for a short while. The reason for their "exodus" was to facilitate Muslim annihilation of the State of Israel and the massacre of Jewish people. When they failed, the Palestinian refugees were never accepted or repatriated into other Muslim countries. They were deliberately kept in the harshness and squalor of refugee camps "to keep their flames of hatred toward the Israelis white hot."

The Jews who resided in Muslim lands for centuries were driven out by savage acts of terrorism and massacre. Those who were able to leave alive were not allowed to take anything with them. All their assets were seized. They were immediately received and repatriated by Israel and the Jewish people.

CHAPTER ELEVEN

The 'Turkeyfication' of Islam: The Enormous Impact of the Ottomans

"The Palestinians who are today's refugees in the neighboring countries know all this—that their present nationalist exploiters are the worthy sons of their feudal exploiters of yesterday, and that the thorns of their life are of Arab, not Jewish origin."

ABDEL RAZAK KADER, 1969

From the Crusades to the Ottoman Turk Empire

Many great movements of history took place during this period that affected both the Islamic Empire and the Christian west.

THE LAST EUROPEAN CRUSADE

The eighth and final European Crusade was led by the King of France. It ended in A.D. 1291 with the fall of the last Christian stronghold in the Holy Land—the port city of Acre (Akko in Hebrew). There would not be another European attempt to liberate the Holy Land for 500 years. Oddly enough, another French king, Napoleon Bonaparte, would launch it. He arrived in 1798. Interestingly, general Napoleon's noble quest failed because he suffered his first military defeat at Acre.

By God's providence, Napoleon's cannons were captured while being transported from Alexandria to Joppa when British Admiral Nelson intercepted and defeated the French navy. Napoleon arrived and was bombarded by his own deadly artillery. Some of his best and bravest soldiers were lost before he gave up and left.

God's hand was in this, for Napoleon had promised his Jewish financiers he would capture the Holy Land and establish the state of Israel. This would have been out of God's predicted timetable; Hebrew prophets prophesied God would bring back the scattered sons of Israel and cause the nation to be born shortly before the coming of the Messiah. That restoration could not happen for another 150 years.

THE MONGOL INVASION OF MUSLIMS

The Mongol tribes united under chief Temujin in A.D. 1206. He was renamed Ghengis Khan, which means "Supreme Ruler". He charged across the Steppes and over the Caucuses Mountains to take on the Muslim Empire.

The formidable Mongol cavalry and fierce warriors were virtually unstoppable. By A.D. 1258, the "golden horde," led by Ghengis Khan's grandson Hulagu Khan, destroyed the Abbasid Khaliphate of Baghdad as well as the Seljuk sultanate in Asia Minor.

The Mongols posed a tremendous threat to Asia, the Middle East and Europe. They were finally defeated by Muslim Mamelukes at the battle of Ain Jalut in A.D. 1260.[1]

The greatest significance of this to my theme is that these events created the circumstances needed for Muslim Ottoman Turks to take control of the Middle East from the Arabs.

ORIGIN OF THE OTTOMAN TURKS

Robert Goldston chronicles the events that set the stage for the Ottomans:

> After the Mongols had passed, a young Turkish mercenary named Othman [Uthman] gathered some of the shattered Seljuks forces together and began to impose order amid ruin. Othman slowly extended his martial law through Asia Minor. After many years of struggle he created the only kind of state feasible amid the wreckage left by the Mongols—a military dictatorship of which he became the first sultan.[2]

In A.D. 1288, Uthman, the first sultan of all Turks, formed the Uthman Muslim Dynasty. It soon became known by its variant name—the Ottoman Empire. Their leaders were called Sultans instead of Khaliphs.

For the next six centuries, thirty-seven descendants of the house of Uthman or Ottoman ruled the Empire. It became one of the largest and richest in history. Of particular interest to us are three of these Sultans.

---

1. Sydney Nettleton Fisher, *The Middle East*, (New York, N.Y.: Alfred A Knoff, Ohio University, 1967) pp. 94–95.

2. Robert Goldston, *The Sword of the Prophet*, (New York, N.Y.: Dial Press, 1979) p. 101.

Sultan *Mehmed al-Fatih* ("The Conqueror") ruled from A.D. 1451 to 1481. He was a brilliant, well-educated man, knowledgeable in Turkish, Arabic, Persian and Greek literature. He loved poetry. He could converse in Serbian and Italian. He had an insatiable thirst for information about Alexander the Great, the Caesars and the Roman Legions. No doubt his study of literature on war and related topics enabled him to field one of the finest armies in history. He established military disciplines and traditions that continued to make the Ottoman army formidable for centuries after his death.

Mehmed's greatest influence was that he conquered the eastern capitol of the old Roman Empire and the center of Byzantine Christianity—Constantinople. It was renamed Istanbul and made the capitol of the Ottoman Empire. A steady influx of Islamic power began and Istanbul became the great center of Islam.

Sultan *Salim al-Yavuz* reigned from A.D. 1512 to 1520. Although he only ruled for eight years, he added more territory to the Islamic Empire than any other Sultan. Most important, though, Salim conquered the Holy Land and Jerusalem for the Ottomans in 1517. They would control this territory until British General Allenby liberated it 400 years later in December of 1917.

Under Sultan *Suleiman* *"the Magnificent,"* who ruled from A.D. 1520 to 1586, the Ottoman Empire reached its zenith of power and glory. During his reign, the Ottoman Empire extended northward to include Greece, modern Bulgaria, Romania, Hungary and the Balkans in what would become modern Yugoslavia. The empire controlled the Mediterranean coast from Egypt to Morocco; the Sudan and all of Middle East, including Arabia; the territories of Syria, Persia, Afghanistan and India. Twice they nearly conquered Vienna.

Suleiman rebuilt Jerusalem and its ancient walls which exist to this day. But from Suleiman's reign onward, the Ottoman Empire began a slow and steady decline. The Sultans that followed were more interested in the size of their harems than the state of their kingdom. The Empire drifted from Koranic dynamism to corrupt despotism.

✻ Question Claire had (or comment re: claim on Israel)

The Ottoman Empire's Affect on the Middle East

Robert Goldston notes a significant development within the Muslim world of this time:

> The Ottoman Turks were not, and never considered them-selves to be, part of the Arab world. [They were] a cos-mopolitan regime whose rulers looked upon all peoples— Bulgarians, Egyptians, Greeks, Syrians, Romanians, Persians, Lebanese, Jews and Arabs—as subject nations to be gov-erned from, and for the benefit of, the Turkish homeland in Asia Minor. To Arabs, as to Europeans, the Ottoman Turks were essentially foreign masters.[3]

Understanding this condition, which resulted from the Otto-man's attitude about the lands and peoples they ruled, is key. *They literally obliterated the state identities and boundaries of the Middle East. For the next four centuries, there were no nation-states such as Syria, Lebanon, Iraq/Babylon, Arabia, Persia, etc.* They were simply terri-tories ruled by Ottoman Viziers from major cities.

Palestine, for instance, included what is now known as Syria, Lebanon, Jordan and Israel, and was ruled from Damascus. There were no independent Arab nations and no defined boundaries.

Remember this, for when the British liberated the area from the Ottoman Turks, no Arab had any more valid claim to a specif-ic land or state than the Jews did. As a matter of fact, the Jews had a mandate of specific land ratified by the League of Nations. Not one Arab state could claim this kind of ratification from such a world authority.

BRITAIN SEEKS TO SECURE THE LAND BRIDGE

By the middle of the nineteenth century, Sultan 'Abdul'l-Majid Khan I (1839–61), the thirty-first Sovereign of the House of Osman, was desperately trying to halt the slide of his empire into

---

3. Ibid., p. 101–104.

oblivion. At this time, long before they teamed up with czarist Russia in an alliance against Germany and Turkey, Britain and France were interested in maintaining the Ottoman Empire for geo-strategic reasons and began applying pressure on Istanbul.

The British had an almost inordinate fear of Russia or Germany controlling the "strategic land bridge" connecting the continents of Europe, Asia and Africa. This land bridge begins in the north at the Bosporus straights in Istanbul and extends southward through Turkey, Syria, Lebanon, Israel and Sinai—ending at the Suez Canal. They rightly believed it was absolutely necessary to control this area. If the land bridge fell into the hands of a hostile power, Britain's vital link to its most-valued colony, India, would be threatened.

RELIEF FOR THE DHIMMIS

Though the Ottoman Turks were not Arabs, they were infected with the Arab hatred of Jews and Christians through the Koran and Muslim traditions. They applied the Islamic Dhimmi laws with calloused cruelty.

Fortunately, because of continuous European influence from 1847 through about 1880, there was a brief relaxation of institutionalized and legalized repression against Jews and Christians in the Ottoman Empire, especially in the Holy Land.

Here are excerpts from observations made by a Polish traveler in Palestine around A.D. 1850:

> O brothers of Israel, how can I convey to you the harshness of the yoke of exile that our brethren living in Palestine suffered prior to the year 1847: Even were I to relate everything, would it be credible? It was a great danger for Jews to venture even a few yards outside the gates of Jerusalem because of the Arab brigands. They were accustomed to say Ashlah Yahudi, that is: "Strip yourself, Jew," and any Jew caught in such a predicament, seeing their aggressiveness and weapons, would strip, while they divided the spoil between them and sent him away naked

and barefoot. They call this spoil: Kasb Allah, that is, Allah's reward.

Moreover, the seven-hour journey from Jerusalem to Hebron was fraught with danger even with a large caravan, and all the more so was a trip to smaller towns. To this day it is customary to recite a thanksgiving prayer when arriving safely at a town from another. If a Jew encounters a Muslim in the street and passes on the latter's right, the Muslim says ishmal, that is, "Pass on my left side." If he touches him or bumps into him, and especially if he stains his clothing or shoes, then the Muslim attacks him cruelly and finds witnesses to the effect that the Jew insulted him, his religion and his prophet Muhammad, with the result that a numerous crowd of Muslims descend upon him and leave the Jew practically unconscious. Then they carry him off to jail, where he is subjected to terrible chastisement.

There are many more such sufferings that the pen would weary to describe. These occur particularly when we go to visit the cemetery and when we pray at the Wall of Lamentations, when stones are thrown at us and we are jeered at.[4]

MORE RESTRICTIONS ON JEWS

Though reforms made life slightly more tolerable for Jews and Christians in the Holy Land, local Muslims resented edicts from Istanbul and often disregarded them. In addition, the reforms did not last. Faced with a budding Zionist movement urging the return of Jews to Palestine, Istanbul repealed the reforms and enacted more restrictive laws against Jews.

In 1887, a law was passed forbidding Jews to immigrate into Palestine, to reside there, to buy land, to restore houses, or to live in Jerusalem. It applied only to Jews—not to Christians or Muslim immigrants.[5]

---

4. Bat Ye'or, *The Dhimmi*, (Farleigh Dickinson University Press, 1985), pp. 371–372.
5. Ibid., pp. 107–108.

THE 'PALESTINIANS FROM BOSNIA-HERZEGOVINA'

To counteract the effect of some of the Jewish emigration that took place between 1847 and 1880, Ottoman authorities began an affirmative action program to resettle European Muslims in Palestine. While Arabs often make much of the European Heritage of many of Israel's Jews—calling them "foreign invaders"—the truth is many of today's so-called Palestinians have European roots going back only a generation or two.

During the latter stages of the receding Ottoman Empire, beginning around 1878, Muslim refugees from the lost Islamic provinces of Europe streamed into Palestine. Writes author Bat Ye'or:

> The Ottoman government settled these emigrants in troubled regions, thereby tightening its control through a policy of Muslim colonization. In 1878 after annexation of *Bosnia-Herzegovina by Austria, Bosnian Muslim colonists arrived in Macedonia and on the coastal plain of Palestine.*[6]

OTTOMAN DESOLATION OF HOLY LAND

The Holy Land under the Ottoman Turks suffered more devastation in four hundred years than the previous fifteen hundred. By the nineteenth century, the ancient canal and irrigation systems were destroyed. The land was barren and filled with malaria-ridden swamps. The hills were denuded of trees and brush so all of the terraces and topsoil had eroded away, leaving only rocks.[7]

Mark Twain described the Holy Land he visited in 1867:

> Stirring scenes . . . occur in the valley (of Jezreel) no more. There is not a solitary village throughout its whole extent—not for 30 miles in either direction. There are two or three small clusters of Bedouin tents, but not a single permanent habitation. One may ride 10 miles hereabouts

---

6. Ibid., p. 108, emphasis added.

7. Joan Peters, *From Time Immemorial*, (New York: Harper & Rowe, 1984), p.152.

and not see 10 human beings.[8]

How accurately this describes the conditions Ezekiel and other prophets predicted the land would suffer.

THE CURSE OF THE TURK 'EFFENDIS'

With the horrible condition of the land in the late nineteenth century, most Muslim inhabitants of the "Holy Land" were eager to leave if a buyer for their property could be found.

Perhaps the greatest ingredient to the final desertification of Palestine was the practice of the landlord class—the effendis—exploiting Muslim peasants who worked the fields. In some cases, to buy seeds, the peasant farmer would have to pay 200 to 300 percent interest.[9]

When the debts reached an unbearable level, the Muslim peasant farmer would pack up his meager belongings and join a band of Bedouins. The land was then left without care and became despoiled because its owners, absentee Ottoman effendi landlords, only cared about profit and seldom left the luxury of Istanbul to check on their real estate.

The Amazing Jewish Reclamation

From the 1880s through 1918, Jews returning to Palestine faced a harsh life in a barren, Malaria-infested land. Still they came, and by the turn of the century, Jewish villages dotted the countryside. A few years later, Jews represented a majority of the population in Jerusalem. There was new life in Haifa, Safed and Tiberias. In 1909, the first modern all-Hebrew city was founded on the sands of the Mediterranean—Tel Aviv.

Far from being run off the land, the Muslim population bene-

---

8. Mark Twain, The Innocents Abroad (London: 1881) p. 349.
9. Ibid., p. 167.

fited greatly from these developments. Quickly, opportunities arose for three Arab groups:

- The landless population looking for work

- The people indebted to the absentee landlords

- The Effendis themselves, who sold land to the Jews at astronomical prices.[10]

THE 'EFFENDIS' SOW SEEDS OF MIDDLE EAST CRISIS

The Effendis collected taxes for the Turkish administration and controlled the populace from their seats on governing councils. But, before long, many of them saw their little feudal empires threatened by the growing influence of the Jews. So, they resorted to the age-old tactic that always worked in Muslim history—make the Jews scapegoats.

Historian Joan Peters writes:

> It was in 1909, at the time when leading effendis felt their grip over the lives and fortunes of their erstwhile prey was getting too loose, that effendi Ruhi Bey al-Khalidi warned that the Jews would "displace the Arab farmers from their land and their fathers' heritage. The Jews were not here when we conquered the country." It mattered little that the effendi's argument was false. It served his group's long-range economic interests, and at least some of his misstatements would be swallowed whole by a surprisingly large part of the world for the better part of a century.[11]

> Those few "Arab effendi" families . . . who had been dispossessing and then continuing to exploit the hapless peasant/migrant in underpopulated Palestine would become threatened by the spectacle of "dhimmi Jews" living on the land as equals, tilling their own soil and granting

---

10. Ibid., p. 201.

11. Ibid., p. 213.

previously unknown benefits to the Arabic-speaking non-Jewish worker. The Jews would undoubtedly upset the "sweets of office" which had been accruing to the effendis. Thousands of peasant-migrants would be emigrating to reap the better wages, health benefits and improvements of the Jewish communities. Although the effendis would charge scalper's prices for land they sold to the Jews, at the same time they would lose thousands of their former debtors who saw an escape from the stranglehold of usury and corruption prevalent in Palestine for generations.

In short, in "Palestine", the greatest exploitations and injustices against the peasant-migrant Muslims were committed against them by their "brother" Muslim effendis.[12]

The Jews became a victim of their own success. The more they restored the land and made it fertile, the more Muslims were attracted from nearby countries. They flocked to Jewish-settled areas for jobs. These same poor Muslims who benefited from the Jewish jobs later charged the Jews had stolen their land, which had been in their families since time immemorial. This remains one of the most colossal lies of history. Yet, the West has bought the lie without questioning its veracity. This will eventually lead to Armageddon.

Effect of World War I on Palestine

During World War I, it became clear to the Zionist leaders—Chaim Weizmann, Zeev Jabotinsky and Aaron Aaronson—that working through the Ottoman Empire, now at war with its one-time protector Britain and the allied powers, was a no-win situation.

Author Samuel Katz explains:

Each independently came to the conclusion that Jewish restoration could be built only on the ruins of the Ottoman Empire. Each in his own way sought to provide Britain and her allies with help to win the war.[13]

---

12 .Ibid., p. 173.

13. Samuel Katz, *Battleground: Fact & Fantasy in Palestine,* (New York, N.Y.: Steimatzky & Shapolsky, 1985), p. 120.

The alliance with Britain during World War I, which was critical to the allies' success in the Middle East campaign, was not without some heavy risks for the Jews. By this time, the considerable Jewish population in Palestine under Turkish rule would be in great peril if they were perceived as anti-Turkish.

"Fear of Turkish reprisals . . . was overcome, however, by a more powerful emotion–the urge to national regeneration," writes Katz.[14]

What did the Jews contribute to the successful allied war effort? A Jewish legion was formed to fight within the British Army for the liberation of Palestine. A Jewish auxiliary unit, the Zion Mule Corps, took part in the Gallipoli campaign. Jewish battalions, comprised of volunteers from Britain, the United States, Canada and Palestine took part in general Allenby's ultimate liberation of the Holy Land. Meanwhile, in Palestine, Aaronson organized the Nili group, an indispensable intelligence service for the British behind Turkish lines.[15]

THE TERRIBLE EFFECT OF THE LAWRENCE OF ARABIA MYTH

Movie fans might ask at this point: "Well, what about Lawrence of Arabia? Wasn't the Arab revolt key to the liberation of the Middle East from the Turks?" To get the truth on this issue, you have to forget the magnificent movie beautifully acted by Peter O'Toole, Anthony Quinn and Omar Sharif. It was great entertainment, but far from the truth.

Once again, Hollywood helped perpetuate a gross myth on the public with its glorification of young British army officer T. E. Lawrence and his largely fabricated Arab revolt.

Stunned by early military disaster on the shores of Gallipoli, some British diplomatic and military leaders got the brilliant idea to bring vast areas of the Arab-speaking world, now under Otto-

---

14. Ibid., p. 121.
15. Ibid., p. 121–123.

man rule, under British control after the war. They envisioned "a federation of semi-independent Arab states under European guidance and supervision . . . owing spiritual allegiance to a single Arab prelate, and looking to Great Britain as patron and protector."[16]

HOW THE BRITISH SET UP
THE MIDDLE EAST CRISIS

The British were to receive a lesson from the age-old Arab adage: "Promise an Arab an centimeter and he will demand a kilometer."

Another gross British misunderstanding was with the Muslim religious power structure. The Sherif of Mecca did not have the same authority and control over Islam as the Pope does over the Roman Catholic Church. Yet this was the basic assumption on which their planned control of the Arabs depended. The Turks had destroyed the Arab Khaliphate in Mecca centuries before—so the Arabs had no central authority with which to deal. There was only a horde of warring tribes wanting to get the best deal in the great land grab following the collapse of the Ottoman Empire.

Britain's first step in achieving its glorious imperial ambition was to enlist Arabs in their fight against the Turks. The first contact was with Hussein ibn-Ali, Sherif of Mecca. Hussein was promised much of Arabia and vast amounts of gold and arms if he led a revolt against the Turks.

A key player in what ensued was Lt. Col. T. E. Lawrence, an ambitious and imaginative officer who dramatized and embellished his own heroics in the desert. This self-aggrandizement helped create the myth that the Arabs played a key role in the British campaign.

Indeed the one significant contribution of the Arab revolt was the capture of Aqaba. But Lawrence did not lead this campaign. It was led by Auda abu Tayi, the sheikh of the Howeitat tribe (played by Anthony Quinn in the movie). Lawrence was permitted by

---

16. Ibid., p. 46.

Auda to ride along with the Bedouin army. But by the time Lawrence returned to British headquarters, he was claiming a personal military triumph.

Nevertheless, it was not until 1955 that British writer Richard Aldington exposed the Lawrence story as false.

BRITISH FOREIGN OFFICE USES THE MYTH

Even though they knew the Lawrence affair was a fable, the British Foreign Office used it for their own purposes. They pursued their imperial dreams for the Middle East with a policy of befriending and rewarding the Arabs. This erroneous policy laid the groundwork for the Muslims to claim more of the land originally given to the Jews by the League of Nations at the Conference of Remo in 1921–22.

The general staff of the British army knew the Arab revolt contributed little to their victory, *still they allowed the British Foreign Office to negotiate with the Arabs on the premise that they earned the right to have independent states under British control.* All of this predicated on the lie of "their great contribution to the war effort."

This policy caused enormous problems later when the Arabs pressed demands upon the British to stop Jewish immigration into Palestine. Incredibly, again on the basis of the Lawrence of Arabia fiction, most British Foreign Office officials thought they owed this favor to the Arabs. In fact, many Jews went to Hitler's gas ovens because of the immigration restrictions implemented.

The allied victory in World War I and the liberation of the Holy Land made it possible for Jews to shake off the vestiges of dhimmi oppression and second-class citizenship in their homeland. But in spite of their contributions to that victory, the Jews would face myriads of problems leading to the Middle East crisis we see today. We can thank the Middle East section of the British Foreign Office for the chaos that follows.

CHAPTER TWELVE

England Awakens to Bible Prophecy

"Where is your Christianity if you do not believe in their Judaism? On every altar . . . we find the table of the Jewish law . . . All the early Christians were Jews . . . every man in the early ages of the Church by whose power or zeal or genius the Christian faith was propagated, was a Jew. . . . If you had not forgotten what you owe to this people . . . you as Christians would be only too ready to seize the first opportunity of meeting the claims of those who profess their religion."

BRITISH PRIME MINISTER BENJAMIN DISRAELI

"The Jewish race, so wonderfully preserved, may yet have another stage of national existence opened

*to them, may once more obtain possession of their
native land . . . The soil of Palestine still enjoys
her sabbaths, and only waits for the return of her
banished children . . ."*

LORD LINDSAY, MEMBER OF PARLIAMENT, 1847

---

1. Joan Peters, *From Time Immemorial* (New York, N.Y.: Harper & Row, 1984), p. 91.

To fully appreciate the miracle of Israel's rebirth in the modern world, the motivations of its on-again off-again sponsor, England, require examination

England had a long fascination with the Holy Land, dating back to its earliest days of Christianity. While Peter brought the Christian faith to Rome, resentful former Roman subjects in England contended it was Joseph of Arimathea who first evangelized the British Isles and, thus, brought an original, first-hand understanding of the Gospels with him.

In search of their spiritual roots and, perhaps, their sense of nationality, the British spent several hundred years trying to conquer the Holy Land by brute, military force in the name of Christianity. Generation after generation of England's best and brightest young men were sacrificed in bloody crusades determined to capture Jerusalem.

The Literal Bible Interpretation Factor

It wasn't until the seventeenth century and the early stirrings of the Puritan movement that attitudes toward Jews shifted. The impact of the sixteenth century Reformation was having an effect, especially on Puritans. A major contribution of the Reformation was the recovery of literal or "normal" interpretation of Scripture. However, it took awhile for the theologians to apply literal meaning to Bible prophecy, as Jesus and the Apostles had done. As soon as they did, Israel and the Jewish people were seen in an entirely new light. In England, the Puritans were the first to diligently study Bible prophecy using this reformed method. They began to understand the special relationship that existed between Jews and their promised land.

In 1948, the Jewish state was reborn, due in large measure to the spiritual vision of British students of prophecy. The large Bible conferences they held influenced the whole nation—even some members of Parliament.

It was a different story back in 1649, when Jews were officially forbidden from residing in England, and had been for some 350 years. But that year, two English Puritans, Joanna and Ebenezer Cartwright, petitioned the government to repeal the ban and organized an effort to transport European Jews to the Holy Land and restore the nation of Israel.

> That this Nation of England, with the inhabitants of the Netherlands, shall be the first and the readiest to transport Israel's sons and daughters in their ships to the Land promised to their forefathers, Abraham, Isaac and Jacob for an everlasting inheritance [is our purpose].[2]

The Puritans took the Bible seriously—both the Old and New Testament. They were quick to see the prophecies regarding the Second Coming of Christ all presupposed a reborn-Jewish state comprised of people who had been scattered into "every nation throughout the world."

ENGLAND AS A WAY STATION

But there were no Jews in England. So as a pre-requisite to fulfillment of prophecy, the British Puritans believed it necessary to bring Jews into their country from Holland. Many Jews who fled Spain and Portugal settled and flourished in Holland. Nevertheless, the Puritans were not totally free of prejudices and misguided ideas Crusaders had developed about the Jews. They believed they had to convert the Jews to Christianity and then they could transplant them to the Holy Land. They failed to see that prophecies like Ezekiel's clearly showed the Israelites would not come to faith in the Messiah until the state of Israel was miraculously reborn.

As Tuchman explains it:

> The movement was not for the sake of the Jews, but for the sake of the promise made to them. According to Scripture the kingdom of God for all mankind would come when the people of Israel were restored to Zion. Only

---

2. Barbara W. Tuchman, *Bible and Sword*, (New York; Ballantine Publishers, 1984), p. 121.

then would the world see the advent of the Messiah or, in Christian terms, the Second Advent.[3]

They saw the remigration in terms of an ethnically Jewish nation converted to Christianity. Therefore, the Jews must first come to England. The Puritans were certain if brought under their influence, the Jews would be persuaded Jesus was their Messiah. After all, they reasoned, the Puritans were fluent in Hebrew and the Old Testament traditions and rituals. How could they fail?

PURITANS' USE OF OLD TESTAMENT

The Puritans of that era, a people who shared the ancient Hebrews experience of persecution, were indeed captivated by the Old Testament. Historian T.B. Macauley notes:

> They baptized their children by the names not of Christian saints but of Hebrew patriarchs and warriors. They turned the weekly festival by which the church had from primitive times commemorated the resurrection of the Lord, into the Jewish Sabbath. They sought for precedents to guide their ordinary conduct in the books of Judges and Kings.[4]

Imagine that! In mid-seventeenth century England, names like Mary and John were dismissed for Old Testament favorites like Enoch, Amos, Obadiah, Job, Seth, Eli, Esther and Rebecca! None of the Old Testament names were overlooked. There are records of English Puritans named Zerrubabel, Habakkuk and even Shadrack, Meshach and Abednego.[5]

These individuals were earnest Bible scholars. Some of them were said to rise at 3 or 4 A.M., eat a raw egg and study the Scriptures until evening. Not surprisingly, it was in this sober Christian environment believers began to understand the prophecies of the end times, especially those concerning Israel.

---

3. Ibid., p. 122.

4. Thomas B. Macauley, *History of England*, vol. 1, (Philadelphia, PA.: 1861) p. 71.

5. Tuchman, *Bible and Sword*, p. 132.

JEWS SHARE THE VISION

The Jews of the mid-1600s also began to think the time was right to live out that old hope, "next year in Jerusalem." Manasseh ben Israel, a respected rabbi in Amsterdam, became convinced the first step toward the fulfillment of Israel's rebirth was immigration to England. Like the Puritans, he believed the Jewish Diaspora must reach every nation before the return to the Holy Land began.

Partly because he was caught up in the prophetic fervor, and partly for strategic and economic reasons related to his war with Holland and Portugal, Oliver Cromwell exhorted his Parliament to aid in the restoration of the Jewish nation. He reasoned, "Truly you are called by God as Judah was to rule with Him and for Him. You are at the edge of the Promises and Prophecies." [6]

The Parliament did not agree. They couldn't have because it was not God's time. The rebirth of Israel was still centuries away. It had to happen in concert with the entire predicted scenario, and that was not yet present.

However, all was not lost. Though Parliament refused to go along with all of Cromwell's program, the ban of Jewish immigration to England was tacitly disregarded. England proved a haven for Jews during and after England's war with Spain in 1656.

> The first stirrings in Puritan England of interest in the restoration of Israel were unquestionably religious in origin, born out of the Old Testament reign over the mind and faith of the party in power during the middle years of the seventeenth century. But religion was not enough.

No practical results would have come out of the Puritans' ability to relate with the children of Israel, or out of their ideals of tolerance, or out of their mystical hopes of hastening the millennium, had not political and economic expediency intervened.

Cromwell's interest in Manasseh's proposal was spurred by the same factor that dictated Lloyd George's interest in Chaim

---

6. Ibid., p. 141.

Weizmann's proposition ten generations later, namely, the aid each believed the Jews could render in wartime. From Cromwell's time, every future episode of British concern with Palestine depended on the twin presence of the profit motive, (whether commercial, military or imperial), and the religious motive inherited from the Bible.[7]

THE NEXT ATTEMPT

The great British scientist, Sir Isaac Newton (A.D. 1643–1727), was a visionary who initiated the literal interpretation of prophecy. He was one of the first scholars to study prophecy as something other than a collection of allegories, symbols, poems and meaningless metaphors that had already been fulfilled. After a lifetime of studying Bible prophecy, he predicted, "About the time of the End, a body of men will be raised up who will turn their attention to the prophecies, and insist on their literal interpretation in the midst of much clamor and opposition."

As one who has been part of the fulfillment of this prediction, I can testify there is plenty of opposition to the insistence that Bible prophecy is going to be literally fulfilled—and sooner than you think!

The far-reaching revival of interest in prophecy that occurred at the beginning of the nineteenth century greatly effected the general population of England. Even some of the aristocracy, who later became high government officials, were deeply effected. This revival was the direct result of literal interpretation of the Bible that began with the Reformation under Luther and spread to the Puritans. It took longer for this method to be applied to prophecy, but by the early eighteen hundreds, it was in full bloom.

Many camp meetings were set up annually to pursue and learn about Bible prophecy. Such articulate luminaries in this movement as John Darby and Sir Robert Anderson spoke to large crowds about the sudden coming of Jesus Christ for His Church. They also linked

---

7. Ibid., p. 146.

the return of God's ancient people to the Holy Land as an indispensable part of the final scenario. They not only believed in a literal rebirth of the State of Israel, but insisted that God's purpose for the Jew as a people and a nation, which was promised throughout the Old Testament, would be fulfilled.

LORD SHAFTSBURY AND LORD ALBERT LINDSEY

Earlier, I discussed how England intervened with Sultan Abdul'l-Majid in 1840 on behalf of the Jews living in the Holy Land. The decision to prod the Turks toward more humane treatment and acceptance of the Jews was inspired by Anthony Ashley Cooper, the seventh Earl of Shaftesbury, an Englishman who believed deeply in the promises of the Bible and their literal meaning.

Besides promoting the restoration of Israel, this Bible-believing Christian is credited by historians with pushing through Parliament laws that dramatically improved working and living conditions for the wretched poor of England. In fact, that is what Lord Shaftesbury is most remembered for. But he also worked diligently on behalf of those he called reverently, "God's ancient people."[8]

Belief in the Second Coming of Jesus Christ "has always been a moving principle of my life, for I see everything going in the world subordinate to this great event," he told his biographer. He confidently believed, on the basis of Scriptural evidence, the return of the Jews was indispensable to the Second Coming.[9]

But Shaftesbury, like his contemporary evangelicals and his seventeenth century Puritan forebearers, still believed the Jews must be converted before Israel could or would be reborn. He believed Israel should be restored under the aegis of the Anglican Church. He foresaw the day when a converted Jew would preside as the consecrated Anglican bishop in Jerusalem. This effort, obviously, did not meet with a great deal of success.

---

8. Ibid., p. 178.
9. Ibid.

Interestingly, Shaftesbury and his contemporaries were persuaded of the role of the Jews in restoring Israel by the books of Lord Albert Lindsey, who wrote eloquently about how the barrenness and decay of the Holy Land was due to the "removal of the ancient inhabitants."[10]

Lord Lindsey wrote:

> The Jewish race, so wonderfully preserved, may yet have another stage of national existence opened to them, they may once more obtain possession of their native land. The soil of Palestine still enjoys her Sabbaths, and only waits for the return of her banished children, and the application of industry, commensurate with her agricultural capabilities, to burst once more into universal luxuriance, and be all that she ever was in the days of Solomon.[11]

Shaftesbury and other British evangelicals of his day were also influenced by the Frenchman Napoleon Bonaparte, who, in 1799, pledged to conquer Palestine and "restore the country to the Jews." He, of course, had failed.

NOT FOR NAUGHT

The efforts of these noble men were not fruitless. England took up the cause of restoring Israel once more in the early twentieth century. But Lord Balfour's declaration would not have been possible without the strong biblical case made for Israel by the British Protestant Bible Prophecy movement in the seventeenth and nineteenth centuries.

Following Lord Shaftesbury, another Englishman became taken by the idea of restoring Israel. Benjamin Disraeli, who would rise to become prime minister, was one of the most provocative figures in British history. A Jewish convert to Christianity, he was more concerned with the world's debt to the Jews than the Jews' future

---

10. Ibid., p. 213.

11. Joan Peters, *From Time Immemorial*, p. 91.

in the world. In 1878, Disraeli recaptured Cyprus for Britain and purchased Suez—both, geographically speaking, a mere stone's throw from the Holy Land. Disraeli knew it was just a matter of time.

MEET LORD BALFOUR

The next British leader to pursue the vision was Arthur James Balfour, who, as England's foreign minister, signed the famous Balfour Declaration mandating the recreation of the Jewish state. He, too, believed religion, and civilization in general, owed Judaism "an immeasurable debt, shamefully ill repaid."[12]

Freshly deposed as Prime Minister in 1906, Balfour set out on a personal mission. Having met Chaim Weizmann, the leader of the Zionist movement (who would one day be Israel's first head of government), Balfour saw an opportunity not only to bring the Holy Land back to life but, as he put it, of "doing something material to wash out an ancient stain upon our own civilization."[13]

His motivations were made even more clear in a speech he delivered to House of Lords in 1922:

> This is the ideal which chiefly moves me . . . that Christendom is not oblivious to their faith, is not unmindful of the service they have rendered to the great religions of the world, and that we desire to the best of our ability to give them the opportunity of developing in peace and quietness under British rule, those great gifts which hitherto they have been compelled to bring to fruition in countries which know not their language and belong not to their race.[14]

While Lord Balfour's motivations were clear, the motives of others responsible for the mandate and what followed were more suspect. The World War I campaign in the Middle East was of paramount concern. And the Jews had much to offer—strategically and militarily.

---

12. Ibid., p. 311.
13. Ibid., p. 316.
14. Ibid.

In 1917, Britain's Palestine policy was being shaped by many hands—from Cabinet ministers to bureaucrats. Nevertheless, on October 13, the Cabinet authorized the Foreign Secretary to issue the Balfour Declaration promising the Jews a homeland after the war.

A few days later, the *London Times* published a story about a celebration by the British Zionist Federation:

> Its outstanding features were the Old Testament spirit which pervaded it and the feeling that, in the somewhat incongruous setting of a London theater, the approaching fulfillment of ancient prophecy was being celebrated with faith and fervor.

"It was appropriate that it should be," concludes David Fromkin. "Biblical prophecy was the first and most enduring of the many motives that led Britons to want to restore the Jews to Zion."[15]

In the next chapter, however, we will see how those good motives were hijacked on the way to Jerusalem.

---

15. David Fromkin, *A Peace to End All Peace* (New York, N.Y.: Avon), p. 298.

CHAPTER THIRTEEN

Britain's Betrayal: The Sellout of the Jews

"This land is capable of supporting a large population if irrigated and cultivated scientifically . . . The Zionists have as much right to this no-man's land as the Arabs, or more."

HISTORIAN ARNOLD TOYNBEE, 1918
(COMMENTING ON AREAS KNOWN TODAY AS ISRAEL AND JORDAN)

"If we must have preferences, let me murmur in your ear that I prefer Arabs to Jews."

ANTHONY EDEN, BRITISH SECRETARY OF FOREIGN AFFAIRS[1]

---

1. Barbara W. Tuchman, *Bible And Sword*, (New York, N.Y.: Ballantine Publishers, 1984), p. 339.

Review of Elements of Betrayal

Of all the injustices perpetrated against Jewish people in the Holy Land, the worst is how their country has been continually reduced from its original mandated size. This is not an isolated case. Throughout the ages, Israel had endured much by many countries. Let's chronicle events presented thus far.

There has continually been a sizable Jewish remnant living in the Holy Land despite the Roman destruction in A.D. 70 and the crushing of Jewish rebellions in the second century A.D. In the eighteenth and nineteenth centuries, Jews actually outnumbered Muslims in Jerusalem.

During the four centuries under Ottoman Turkish control, the Holy Land reached its ultimate state of desolation. The absentee landlords, known as *effendis*, practiced such calloused usury and taxation on the poor Arab farmers they were eventually overwhelmed with debt and fled the land. By the beginning of the nineteenth century, every report from the Holy Land spoke of the absence of any settled people apart from a few villages and towns. Their remarks call attention to the terrible condition of the land and the vast desolation between villages.

We have also seen the Arab-Muslim world of the nineteenth century Middle East was without national entities. All semblances of independent states and nationalism were crushed during the harsh Ottoman occupation. All that was left were the Tribal sheikdoms that warred with each other constantly, and the small Arab Hashemite Kingdom that controlled Mecca and Medina.

WHENCE COMETH THE PALESTINIANS?

There was no Palestinian state or people known as "Palestinians." The few Arabic-speaking people living there considered themselves "Ottomans", "Turks", "Southern Syrians" or simply "Arab people", but never "Palestinians." The migratory Bedouins who seasonally moved through the area never laid claim to the land.

The Jews, who began returning to the Holy Land in earnest throughout the mid-nineteenth century, bought land from the all-to-willing-to-sell effendis for enormously inflated prices.

With the price of Herculean labor and the loss of many lives to malaria, the Jews began to reclaim the land and make it flourish. This development encouraged a significant number of poor Arab-Muslims to flock to there in order to find work and a better standard of living. Jews became victims of their own success. Little did they realize the very ones they were helping would turn and claim Jews had stolen their land that had belonged to Arab families for hundreds of years. While, in fact, most of the so-called Palestinian refugees couldn't establish to UN workers sent to help they had been in Palestine more than two years prior to their 1948 exodus, a pilgrimage designed to clear the way for Arab armies to annihilate the new state of Israel.

THE BALFOUR DECLARATION

Because of the existing conditions in the Middle East, Lord Balfour and other members of the British Parliament thought that setting forth the propositions contained in the Balfour Declaration was not an invasion of Arab-Muslim land. The motto of the forming committee was, "A people for a land, for a land without a people." Furthermore, the League of Nations concurred with the "Declaration" for the same reasons.

The actual Balfour Declaration of 1917 was a rather simple statement committing Britain to work toward the establishment of a Jewish homeland in an area of the vast wasteland designated as the Palestinian territory. It read:

> His Majesty's Government view with favor the establishment in Palestine of a national home for the Jewish people, and will use their best endeavors to facilitate the achievement of this object, it being clearly understood that nothing shall be done which may prejudice the civil and religious rights of existing non-Jewish communities in

Palestine or the rights and political status enjoyed by Jews in any other country.[2]

With its passage in Parliament, Lord Balfour said, "We hope that the 'small notch' of Palestine being given the Jews would not be 'grudged' by the Arab leaders."[3]

Maps 1A and B illustrate what Lord Balfour referred to as "a small notch" of Palestine. They show the borders specifically designated for a Jewish National Homeland by the Balfour Declaration in 1917.

On January 4, 1919, a formal agreement on this mandated Jewish homeland was signed in London. The signatories were: His Royal Highness the Emir Feisal ibn-Hussein, representing and acting on behalf of the Arab Kingdom of Hedjaz, and Chaim Weitzman, representing and acting on behalf of the Zionist Organization.[2]

The Balfour Declaration was the result of a great many debates and compromises within the British government, but, without question, reflected its unequivocal goal at the time. It was clearly and unambiguously understood by representatives of all sides present: A Jewish state was to be established as soon as Jewish immigration and development was sufficient in the barren wilderness of Palestine. Later, all kinds of ridiculous interpretations would be placed on the declaration.

THE LEAGUE OF NATIONS MANDATE

The boundaries of this new nation were codified and approved unanimously by the League of Nations three years after the Balfour Declaration. Britain was given authority over the entire Middle East, from the Mediterranean to the borders of India. The territory

---

2. See the full text of this agreement in Appendix A.

3. From a speech given by Lord Balfour, July 12, 1920 and recorded in the Palestine Royal Commssion Report of 1937, paragraph 27 of page 27, as cited by Joan Peters, *From Time Immemorial*, (New York, N.Y.: Harper & Rowe, 1984), p. 235.

MAP 1A

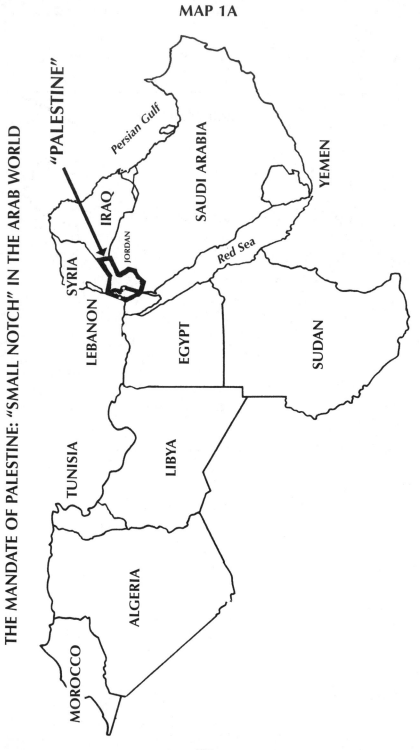

THE MANDATE OF PALESTINE: "SMALL NOTCH" IN THE ARAB WORLD

"PALESTINE"

Persian Gulf

SYRIA

IRAQ

JORDAN

LEBANON

SAUDI ARABIA

YEMEN

Red Sea

EGYPT

SUDAN

TUNISIA

LIBYA

MOROCCO

ALGERIA

MAP 1B

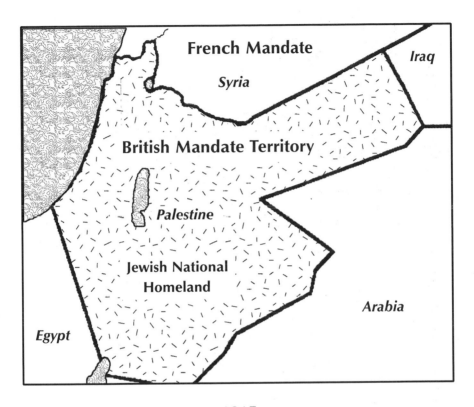

French Mandate

Iraq

Syria

British Mandate Territory

Palestine

Jewish National
Homeland

Arabia

Egypt

1917

The Jewish National Homeland

The Balfour Declaration

to become the state of Israel—then variously referred to as "Palestine," "Western Palestine," "South Syria" or even as part of Turkey—extended east and west of the Jordan River from the Mediterranean to Arabia and Iraq, and north and south from Egypt to Lebanon and Syria. On present day maps, that includes most of the Arab nation of Jordan, southern Lebanon and the Sinai. (See Map 2.)

Simultaneously, independent Arab statehood was being granted in Syria, Iraq and Saudi Arabia. The land originally given was considerably bigger than today's Jewish state, even including the territories captured in June 1967. Evidence shows Arab leaders were initially satisfied with their acquisition and didn't question the status of Jewish Palestine.

In a letter to colonial Secretary Winston Churchill from T. E. Lawrence in January 1921, Emir Feisal, the man who had led the Arab revolt, "agreed to abandon all claim of his father to (Western) Palestine," if he secured Iraq and Eastern Palestine as Arab territories. In fact, Emir Feisal had written, in his own hand, a letter agreeing to exactly this in a 1919 meeting with Zionist representative Chaim Weizmann. (See Appendix A). Furthermore, in an agreement worked out between Weizmann and Feisal, both sides pledged the "closest possible collaboration" and "most cordial goodwill" in detailing the creation of the modern Arab states and Israel.[4] (See Appendix B.)

The Arab's felt magnanimous at the time because they had just emerged from centuries of Ottoman Turkish occupation wherein they owned nothing. Suddenly Britain hands them an enormous gift, and yet they did little to earn it. This is why Lord Balfour could not imagine they would "begrudge the small notch of land" the Jews were given.

---

4. Joan Peters, *From Time Immemorial*, (New York, N.Y.: Harper & Rowe, 1984), p. 421.

MAP 2

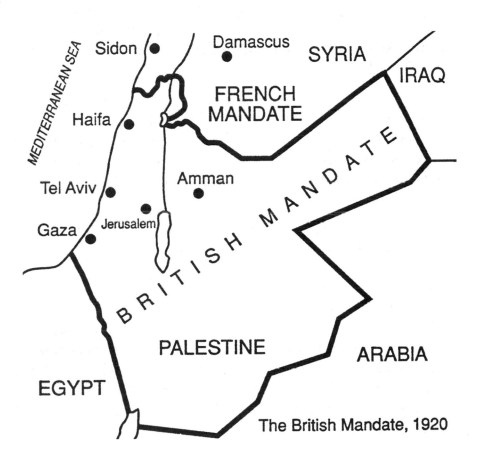

The British Mandate, 1920

Britain Gives Away 75 percent of the Jews' Mandated Land

It wasn't long, however, before Abdullah, brother of Feisal ibn Hussein, decided he should have Transjordan as his Kingdom. He protested to the British who unilaterally decided to carve out of Jewish Palestine 75 percent of its mandated territory, then known as the Transjordan, and hand it over to Abdullah.[5]

It should be explained why Abdullah, who was a Hashemite, was in Transjordan. The tribe of Ibn Saud and his fanatical sect of Wahabi Muslims had just driven the Hashemite Tribe out of Mecca and Medina, taking over the holy sites and all of Arabia. The Hashemites had been custodians of Mecca and Medina for centuries. Feisal, the ruler of the Hashemites, was the one with whom the British Foreign Office made promises to for fighting against the Turks. Abdullah argued the British gave his brother Feisal Ibn Hussein both Syria and Iraq, but gave him nothing. The British Foreign Office quickly scrambled to offer him the major part of land they were bound by the League of Nationd Mandate to give Israel. Recall, this was done on the basis of the fictional T.E. Lawrence story that asserted Abdullah had significantly helped Britain defeat the Ottoman Turks in the Middle East.

> The League of Nations Mandate for Palestine remained unchanged even though Britain had unilaterally altered its map and its purpose. The Mandate included Transjordan until 1946, when that land was declared an independent state. Transjordan had finally become the de jure Arab state in Palestine just two years before Israel gained its Jewish statehood in the remaining one-quarter of Palestine; Transjordan comprised nearly 38,000 square miles; Israel, less than 8,000 square miles."[6] (See Map 3.)

---

5. Ibid., pp. 238–239.
6. Ibid., p. 239.

MAP 3

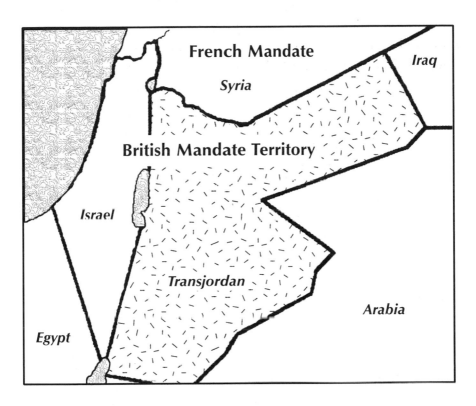

1921

35,000 square miles of the Jewish National Homeland were given to Arabs (80% of their promised land was lost).

BRITAIN VIOLATED ITS MANDATE

When Britain gave Transjordan to Abdullah, it specifically violated Article 5 of the Mandate given unanimous approval by the League of Nations at the San Remo Conference on July 24, 1922. (See Appendix C, plus Map 4, which shows division into Transjordan and Palestine.)

Article 5 stated, "The Mandatory [Britain] shall be responsible for seeing that no Palestine territory shall be ceded or leased to, or in any way placed under the control of, the Government of any foreign Power." Abdullah was a foreign power and certainly not part of the Zionist Organization to whom Transjordan had been given.

The local British officials of the Foreign Office grossly violated the main premise for Britain being given the Mandate by the League of Nations. They were specifically charged with *only* facilitating the immigration of Jews to Palestine to populate and settle the land granted as their homeland. Britain had explicit instructions *not* to allow or facilitate more immigration of Arabs into the new Jewish homeland.

As the following details will show, Britain's actions were contrary to what they were ordered to do. They increasingly restricted Jewish immigration while opening the floodgates to Arab immigration.

THE REAL PALESTINIAN STATE

This historical footnote to the Arab-Israeli conflict serves to shatter another <u>Muslim myth.</u> The modern-day Royal Kingdom of Jordan was and is clearly an independent Palestinian-Arab state. Geographically it spans most of the land once called Palestine. Its population is largely made up of so-called "Palestinians." Abdullah and other Arab leaders admitted as much in 1948 prior to launching their war of aggression against the new state of Israel.

Western media thought Ariel Sharon was being sarcastic and evasive when a newsman asked him if he would give the Palestin-

MAP 4

The British Mandate, 1922

ians a state. He answered, "There already is a state of Palestine— it's called Jordan."[7] It sounded preposterous to the reporters, as most of them had no knowledge of the area's history. But Sharon not only knows that history well, he is a living eyewitness of it.

"Palestine and Transjordan are one, for Palestine is the coast-line and Transjordan the hinterland of the same country," said Abdullah. His Prime Minister, Hazza al-Majali, went even further: "We are the army of Palestine . . . the overwhelming majority of the Palestine Arabs are living in Jordan."[8]

EAST AND WEST PALESTINE

This forgotten concept of "Eastern" and "Western" Palestine is at the root of another Arab fable. As we have already seen, most of the Palestinian population was excluded from the new state of Israel, not by force, but by borders drawn on a map. This is why people accept the idea that Jews forced Palestinians out of their homeland. As seen in earlier chapters, the settled Muslim popula-tion in the Jewish state began growing from the time Jewish emi-gration began in the 1880s through 1948.

As Peters, who conducted a first-hand population study in the region, puts it: "The 'unprecedented' sudden 'natural' increase among Arabs of Western Palestine after centuries of static popula-tion figures was intriguing. That extraordinary increase was repre-sented as a countrywide 'phenomenon.'"[9]

The purpose of Peters' original study was "to determine whether in fact there was a large-scale displacement of Arab natives by Jews in Western Palestine before and at the time of the November 1947-1948 war of Arabs against Jewish independence." Peters admits that when she began the investigation her sympathies were with "Palestinian refugees". She expected to find evidence of Israeli aggression against helpless Palestinians and Israeli occupa-

---

7. Ibid., pp. 238–240.
8. Ibid., p. 240.
9. Ibid., p. 247.

tion of Palestinian family lands.

Peters was astonished at the results. She writes:

> What the calculations indicate is that, rather than a situa-
> tion in which a teeming Arab people, present "from time
> immemorial," was forced off or excluded from its land, the
> situation is almost the exact opposite . . . the Jews,
> whose presence attracted Arab migrants, and the Jews'
> land, earmarked as their home, was usurped by the arrival
> of these Arab in-migrants from outside Jewish-settled areas.[10]

MORE FALSEHOODS DISCOVERED

Peters also found in her original investigation:

* The earlier conservative estimates of Muslim population in the
  Jewish-settled areas of Palestine had been grossly exaggerated.[11]

* Arabs indeed migrated from depressed areas of the region to
  those places where they could gain greater economic advantage
  in Jewish-settled areas.[12]

OVERLOOKING THE OBVIOUS

Why was this factor of explosive Arab population growth not
investigated or considered before? It was because the British never
attempted to count Arab in-migration or illegal migration. They
only quantified Jewish figures from immigration into the Holy
Land, and this they did with scrupulous zeal for details. Furthermore, Peters found, the population was never accurately identified
by location, or analyzed according to Jewish and non-Jewish areas.

Amazingly, false assumptions in subsequent generations have
been that "All Palestine was Jewish-settled" and "Jewish-settled
Palestine was all Arab Palestine." Most of the British Foreign

---

10. Ibid., p. 249.

11. Ibid., p. 251.

12. Ibid., p. 259.

Office could never understand that the Jews came to a land almost entirely barren of settled people of any nationality. A few ignored the facts, blinded by their dislike of Jews.

What made the British turn a blind eye toward this of one-sided population movement? Clearly, within the British Foreign Service there were men who wanted to see the Jewish state fail. In light of their imperial ambitions in the Middle East, they preferred working with the Arabs rather than the more independently minded Jews.

UNDERLINGS SECRETLY REVERSE FOREIGN POLICY OF THEIR NATION

When British General Edmund Allenby walked reverently into Jerusalem, leading his army of liberation on December 9, 1917, he was ready to institute a military government. Unfortunately, virtually the entire staff of Governor Ronald Storrs was riddled with army officers who did not believe in the principles set out in the Balfour Declaration. Without authorization, they reversed the official policy of their government and sabotaged the mandate given by the League of Nations. Had this been discovered and investigated at the time, it would have been considered a crime at best and treason at worst. These men betrayed the official policy of their government.

One example of this group's illegal actions was when Governor Storrs decided to placate the spiritual leader of the Jerusalem Muslims, Haj Amin al-Husseini. You will recall that al-Husseini stayed for a couple of years in Nazi Germany, as the special guest of Adolph Hitler, learning how to deal with "the Jewish problem." The Grand Mufti Husseini, to whom Yasser Arafat is related, used a subtle blend of religious rhetoric, threats, terror and physical violence to get his way. And, as much as he used the British, those pro-Arab Foreign Service officers also tried to use him.

BRITAIN ENACTS HARSHER RESTRICTIONS ON JEWS

From 1920 on, partly as a result of anti-Jewish terrorism, British policy focused almost exclusively on limiting immigration of Jews into Palestine. For the Arabs, a different set of rules applied. *In actuality, British restrictions against Jewish emigration were harsher and more discriminatory than even those of the Turks.*[13]

There were dissenters among the British officers corps—men disgusted by the seemingly official tolerance of Arab violence against Jews. They were ridiculed by their colleagues and over-fulled by their superiors, and then often reassigned, all because an even-handed approach might alienate Arab leaders and jeopardize Britain's imperial plans for Arabia.

THE INFAMOUS WHITE PAPER

By 1930, the British began to rationalize and justify their anti-Jewish policies in Palestine with a series of papers, the first being the Hope-Simpson Report. The report admitted that illicit Arab immigration had, in fact, crowded out many opportunities for Jewish refugees in their designated homeland. But its solution was to deny any more Jewish settlement. Prompted by the 1929 Arab massacres of Jews and other disturbances, it concluded the best way to prevent further bloodshed was to limit Jewish immigration and land purchases even more.[14]

Now that was a splendid display of justice—stop further bloodshed by punishing the victim and rewarding the criminal. It doesn't

13. Ibid., p. 275.
14. Ibid., p. 299.

take a rocket scientist to realize the Arabs would be encouraged to intensify the violence to ultimately get the Jews removed from Palestine altogether "in order to avoid more bloodshed."

THE PASSFIELD-WHITE PAPER

Shortly after the Hope-Simpson Report came the infamous Passfield-White Paper of 1930, which mandated that Jewish emigration would be suspended and that landless Arabs would be given property to cultivate. In the future, the White Paper stated, a resumption of Jewish immigration would depend on an improvement in the Arab employment picture. In effect, the Jews were now being relegated to a permanent minority status, subject only to the future whims of decidedly pro-Arab British officials.

Keep in mind that under the League of Nations mandate, Britain was charged with facilitating the immigration of Jews, not Arabs. Also bear in mind that the British were seeking to give migrant Arabs that which their own Arab brothers had never given them. But the whole process—as usual in the Middle East—was turned upside-down by British administrators who had little or no knowledge of the region's history nor of their mandated mission.

ISRAEL 'DOWNSIZED' AGAIN

By 1937 the situation in Palestine had deteriorated greatly and the British conducted another study. The Royal Commission Report, somewhat more evenhanded than its predecessors, acknowledged the primary purpose of the mandate was to facilitate the creation of a Jewish state. But it also came to the conclusion that the original mandate for the homeland would have to be downsized significantly and partitioned into one Jewish and one Arab state. (See map 4, i.e., the partition into a Jewish and an Arab state in the territory mandated to the Jews.)

The Arabs once again succeeded in slicing off another piece of the area originally given to the Jews by the League of Nations. Never mind that they had been handed 98 percent of the land liberated from the Ottoman Turks. If Israel had a square meter of land in the Holy Land, it was still too much for the Arabs to bear.

ACCESSORIES TO MASS MURDER

Illegal Arab immigration into Palestine continued and the British persisted to place roadblocks in the way of Jewish immigration—even in 1937–38, when wholesale persecution of the prospective colonists by Nazis was under way in Poland and Germany. Adolph Hitler was eager to permit Jews to emigrate, but no nation in the world was willing to accommodate their vast numbers, including the United States, who was in the midst of the Great Depression.

In a 1938 speech, Hitler mocked:

> I can only hope and expect that the other world, which has such deep sympathy for these criminals (Jews), will at least be generous enough to convert this sympathy into practical aid. We on our part, are ready to put all these criminals at the disposal of these countries, for all I care, even on luxury ships.[15]

In spite of the danger posed by Hitler to the Jews, Britain refused to allow more than "very limited" immigration into Palestine.

In fact, a year later in the 1939 White Paper, they reversed the intent of the Balfour Declaration and the League of Nations Mandate. They had the audacity to announce Britain had no intention of facilitating the re-creation of the Jewish state. Why? Because this "would be contrary to our (England's) obligations to the Arabs."[16]

What a lack of honor and character. These very actions are responsible for God destroying the British Empire. Shortly after

---

15. Ibid., p. 333.
16. Ibid., p. 336.

World War II, the mighty world empire of Great Britain became a memory. Remember, God promised Abraham and his descendants, "I will bless those who bless you, and curse those who curse you."

This betrayal by Britian guaranteed Hitler's death camps would be full. It is not an overstatement to say the British policy of appeasement was the direct cause of hundreds of thousands of Jews going to the gas chambers. The British version of the "final solution"—outlined in the 1939 White Paper—would limit Jewish immigration of 10,000 a year for five years at which point it would be terminated unless the Arabs of Palestine were willing to accept more! Is there anyone naive enough to think they would ever accept more when they wanted to annihilate the ones already there?

The leader of the Arabs in Palestine was our "old friend" Haj al-Husseini, who had now been appointed by the British as Grand Mufti of Jerusalem. Since the early 1930s he made no secret of his close affinity for the Nazis and their final solution for the Jews. He kept a copy of Hitler's Mein Kampf next to his Koran.

Haj Amin was, in fact, a pathological murderer who masterminded the killing of Arabs as well as Jews. He would later foment the anti-British, anti-Zionist riots of 1936 through 1939. Eventually he had to flee Palestine, escaping through Iraq to Nazi Germany where he became a confidante to Hitler. He also organized Muslims from Bosnia to fight alongside the elite German Waffen SS troops.[17]

The anti-Jewish attitude among the British had reached its zenith. After the latest restrictions on Jewish immigration were announced, the British cabled their ambassador in Berlin and instructed him to ask the Germans to discourage Jews who might think of illegally traveling to Palestine! That was like pleading with the hangmen not to let their victims escape.

It would not be fair to characterize British policy as reflecting the will of all Englishmen. There were quite a few outspoken lead-

---

17. *Jerusalem Post* International Edition, December 19, 1992, p. 11

ers who harshly criticized their country's betrayal of the Jews. Winston Churchill, for one, saw it as a continuation of Neville Chamberlain's policy of appeasement.

Nevertheless, strict limits on immigration of Jews remained throughout the war. And by 1945, six million Jews had been systematically murdered in Europe. Only 51,000 were permitted to immigrate to Palestine. Incredibly, at the same time, the British continued to wink at illegal immigration into Palestine by the Arabs.

THE TURNING POINT

This was the thanks the Jews got from the British for their loyalty, patience and long-suffering. But the issuance of the White Paper sparked a new attitude among some Zionists. Now the Jews, while fighting alongside the British against the Nazis, would also defy attempts to isolate and neutralize the Jews in Palestine.

It was only through this newfound militancy by Jews—and antidote to the pressure the British were constantly bombarded with by the Arabs—that Israel was reborn in 1948.

Had the British followed their own declaration and the League of Nations mandate they were honor-bound to implement, the rebirth of Israel would have happened sooner.

Had the British enforced their laws against the Muslim effendis' usury, extortion and exploitation of the peasantry instead of defending their anti-Jewish incitements, it would have happened sooner.

Had the British possessed the good sense to allow more Jews to immigrate, the Nazi Holocaust might have been avoided.

THE PRICE OF BRITAIN'S BETRAYAL

Great Britain received a terrible punishment in World War II. London and other major cities were bombed and ravaged by Hitler's Luftwaffe. Before this infamous treatment of Jews and betrayal of the Mandate, "the sun never sat on the British Empire."

Even though the Allies won the war, the British Empire came to an end. Britain is only a shadow of its former glory. This was not a coincidence. It was a direct result of the British betrayal of the Jewish people and the Jewish nation. The God of Abraham, Isaac and Jacob still keeps His Word, **". . . I will curse those who curse you."**

Now, the United States is the main party pushing Israel into a further reduction of land originally allotted to it. We are foolishly pushing them to accept a Palestinian state filled with Muslim terrorists who believe it their duty to destroy Jews for Allah.

The new borders will make Israel indefensible by conventional military means. Once those borders are established, Israel will have only one assurance they will not be attacked—"the promise of the Muslims."

In the interest of a short-term peace, we are guaranteeing a nuclear war. Israel has the "Samson Option" in case Muslim armies overrun them. This "option" will vaporize Arab capitols with thermonuclear bombs.

Are we not doing the same thing the British did, only worse? Let us pray that our leaders will not continue this insane policy, for the God of Israel will certainly keep His word—this time against us.

CHAPTER FOURTEEN

Israel: A Miracle Nation

"This is what the LORD says, he who appoints the sun to shine by day, who decrees the moon and stars to shine by night, who stirs up the sea so that its waves roar—the LORD Almighty is his name: 'Only if these decrees vanish from my sight,' declares the LORD, 'will the descendants of Israel ever cease to be a nation before me.'"

JEHOVAH, THE GOD OF ABRAHAM, ISAAC AND JACOB
JEREMIAH 31:35–36 NIV

"We shall never call for or accept a negotiated peace. We shall only accept war—Jihad—the holy war. We have resolved to drench the lands of Palestine and Arabia with the blood of the infidels or to accept martyrdom for the glory of Allah."

KING ABDUL AZIZ IBN SAUD,
FOUNDER OF THE KINGDOM OF SAUDI ARABIA

The Miracle of Israel's Survival

As discussed in earlier chapters, the original birth and founding of the nation of Israel was a miracle. Its deliverance from Egyptian bondage was a miracle. Its restoration from the Babylonian/Persian captivity was a miracle. Its rebirth in June of 1948 was a miracle. And it's continued survival through four all-out wars—1948–49, 1956, 1967, and 1973, all of which were launched with the combined might of Islam for the express purpose of annihilating Israel and its people—is a miracle, too. Do you begin to see a pattern?

It has been a colossal wonder that the *race* of Israel has persevered. It is equally as great a miracle the modern *state* of Israel has survived. Many have tried to explain Israel's modern endurance in purely natural terms – but frankly, it takes more faith than I have to explain it that way.

The Muslims say it's because Israel has been furnished with so many modern weapons by the US. But the Soviet Union, France, China, etc. have furnished the Muslims with modern weapons as well. The Muslim forces have continually outnumbered the Israelis at least four-to-one, including more modern tanks, aircraft, missiles and artillery.

It is certainly not because individual Israelis are more courageous. Arab-Muslim soldiers are as brave as any in the world. There is only one advantage that stands out for Israelis; they fight more with their reason than with their emotions. And they fight more as a unit than do Muslims.

Examples of Modern Miracles
1967 SIX DAY WAR

An Israeli friend of mine was a young flight leader in the Israeli Air Force during the 1967 Six Day War. He related to me the extremely difficult battle plan they had to execute at the beginning of the war.

They had to coordinate multiple flights of fighter-bombers so all would arrive on target simultaneously. If timing and navigation were off, the war could have been a disaster. Israel's outgunned and outnumbered forces had to seize air supremacy at the beginning to have any chance at all.

Multiple flights of jet fighters screamed toward multiple targets from multiple directions at supersonic speed. The planes flew so low that some took in ocean spray—others were just above the sand dunes. They had to maintain absolute radio silence; no timing coordination or course corrections were possible.

This is my recollection of the account given by my friend:

> I glanced out of the cockpit to glimpse the Nile River streak by underneath. I pulled up lightly to get over a bridge. I was flying so low that I nearly hit the mast of an Egyptian fishing boat. Just three hours before, I was on my honeymoon. A helicopter picked me up off the roof of the hotel. I still remembered waving goodbye to my new bride as she stood on the hotel roof in her negligee.
>
> I went over the battle plan in my mind. The great pyramids of Egypt flashed by off my starboard wing. I looked over my shoulder—all the young pilots were in tight formation behind me. I glanced at my airspeed indicator—Mach .85 "Have to keep just under the sound barrier so as not to set off alarms," I reminded myself. We were counting on the populace thinking we were Egyptian fighters on maneuvers. "One thing for sure," I thought, "at this speed and low altitude, they will never be able to identify the planes. We are gone before they know we were there."
>
> I checked my watch again. "Will we all arrive at the same time?" I wondered. "Will one of the squadrons hit a base early and alert the other bases to launch their fighters?" We had timed the strike to hit just after the Egyptians early morning patrols. "They would be having morning tea about now," I thought.
>
> "Oops! There is my landmark." I instinctively pulled the stick back hard and went into a vertical climb to line up

for attack. "Are we on time? Where are the other squadrons?" I rolled my fighter so that I could see. To my amazement, the other two attack units that had come in from different directions were all climbing in the vertical staring back at me. We had all arrived at the same instant.

I rolled out into a steep dive and screamed down on Egypt's main fighter base just outside of Cairo. There before me was the pride of the Egyptian Air Force parked in neat rows on the airport tarmac. I lined up and dropped my bombs. Three MIGs exploded in fireballs. I whipped my plane around in a tight turn for another pass. My little Mirage fighter's delta wings dug in hard against the g-forces. A large Tupelov bomber filled my gun sight. I fired a quick canon burst and it exploded in flames. In minutes, every aircraft on the Egyptian base was destroyed.

As we turned and streaked across the Sinai for home, I thought, "What a way to enter a war." The Egyptian base was in such chaos that not one shot had been fired at us.

Virtually the entire Egyptian Air Force was destroyed within 30 minutes. Every airfield was hit at approximately the same time. Reconnaissance photos showed at each airfield in Egypt, almost every warplane had been hit dead center.

In six days, the outnumbered Israeli Defense Forces destroyed the combined armies of the Muslim Middle East.

There are some who would say this happened because of superior training. My friend believed that played a part—but God had to have been with us.

1973 YOM KIPPUR WAR

I interviewed a tank commander from the crack Golani Brigade about what happened in the first hours of the Yom Kippur war on the Golan Heights.

On October 6 1973, all Israeli soldiers that could be spared were home on leave for Israel's holiest day of the year, Yom Kippur.

Only a bare minimum force was on duty. Suddenly, at dawn, the entire Syrian border erupted with artillery fire. Fourteen hundred top line Soviet built tanks charged forward. Another 1000 tanks were in reserve. The Syrians had a new anti-tank missile that wreaked havoc with the Israeli tanks.

In response, Israeli air force streaked in low attacking the Syrian ground forces to try and stop the onslaught. A man we'll call Baruch watched in horror as plane after plane was blown out of the sky. The Soviets had designed a new SAM missile for intercepting low flying planes. Israel had no countermeasures for it. This missile wreaked havoc with Israeli planes in both the Sinai and the Golan Heights.

By noon, the Golani tank force had been almost cut to pieces. Baruch commanded the last three remaining tanks which took up position at a critical crossroad for a fight to the death. They knew they were all that stood between the Syrian army and Galilee. Tiberias lay helpless in the path of the invaders' juggernaut. Infamous for their barbaric treatment of Israeli prisoners, Baruch shuttered at the thought of Syrian triumph.

When the Syrian commander could see only three tanks blocking his way, he said "it's too easy—this must be a trap." So he ordered his forces to stop while they analyzed the situation. He reasoned the Israelis were, after all, already beaten.

During the lull, Israeli reinforcements rushed to the front and pushed the Syrian forces back. By a miracle of God, the invaders went no further into Israel—though the horrific fighting continued. The heroic Israeli tank commander attributed their success to God's protective care over Israel.

ISRAEL ALMOST DEFEATED

The Yom Kippur War was not like the Six Day War or any of the previous wars with Muslims. This time Arab armies scored unprecedented and stunning victories. Israeli casualties were the highest yet. Hardened and confident combat units were so outnumbered and outflanked they were fleeing in disarray. Israel lost more than 500 tanks and 49 aircraft in the first three days alone.

My good friend, Congressman Randy Cunningham, was America's leading Vietnam fighter ace at the time. He told me he was one of the pilots in our Mediterranean fleet shuttling aircraft from US carriers to Israel to replace heavy losses. He said as soon as he landed, the Israelis started refueling and arming the plane while painting a Star of David over the US insignia. That's how critical the situation was.

In Sinai, the modernized Egyptian forces used new missiles and electronic defenses to blast their way to the eastern bank of the Suez Canal. Counterattacks by three Israeli tank divisions were repelled.

THE NUCLEAR HOLOCAUST THAT 'ALMOST WAS'

Early on October 8, 1973, Defense Minister Moshe Dayan called Golda Meier and said,

> This is the end of the Third Temple. The situation is desperate—everything is lost. We must withdraw. Arm the "doomsday weapons", I am initiating the "Samson Option."[1]

The Samson Option is a fully operational plan to be used if Muslim forces overrun Israel. If the plan is implemented, every Arab capitol will be vaporized in a thermonuclear mushroom cloud. Only now, the warheads will be delivered by Jericho II missiles instead of aircraft.

Seizing Victory Out of Defeat

The Muslim leaders realized after the Yom Kippur War that another strategy had to be adopted. The leaders surmised Israel could be weakened by reducing its borders to an indefensible size, thus enabling the "Zionist Entity" to be quickly overwhelmed.

---

1. Seymour M. Hersh, *The Samson Option* (New York, N.Y.: Random House, 1991) pp. 222-223.

Additionally, the Muslim world realized they had to match both Israel's nuclear arsenal and its missile delivery systems. They chose to counter with various weapons of mass destruction—chemical and biological as well as nuclear, with missiles to deliver them.

THE NEW KIND OF WAR

Israel is facing a new kind of threat potentially more dangerous than the military threats of the past. The Arab world has successfully framed the debate over the Middle East as a struggle between downtrodden Palestinians and powerful, heavily armed Israelis. Somehow they have convinced the world that Israel, with five million citizens, is bullying the Muslim nations of the Middle East, which have 240 million citizens. And they have covered over the fact that there are over a billion Muslims worldwide sympathetic to their cause.

The new weapons of conquest are carefully crafted propaganda slogans like, "Land for peace!" "The legitimate rights of the Palestinians!" "End the Israeli aggression!" "End the 'occupation' of Palestinian land!"

These familiar pieces of propaganda have been too readily accepted and spread by a Western media which has little concern for the history that put the "lie" to these claims.

The shocking tragedy is that Israelis, like the late Prime Minister Yitzak Rabin and Foreign Minister Shimon Perez, bought into these deceptions and led many others who are understandably tired of war along with them.

More and more Israelis are seemingly willing to be tricked into turning over lands in Judea, Samaria, Gaza and the Golan Heights to the Palestinians in exchange for their promises of peace. For example, the Oslo Agreement set up a suicidal process that could lead to the destruction of Israel according to independent, objective military and intelligence experts.

MINIMUM TERRITORY FOR SURVIVAL

Back in 1967, when the level of military technology and sophistication available to Arab states was much lower than now, a Pentagon study found that Israel needed control of the land east of Jerusalem, the central West Bank territory of the Jordan River and part of the Sinai including Sharm e-Sheikh to survive an Arab assault. More recently, intelligence expert Joseph de Courcy concluded, "The absolute minimum territory Israel requires to deter war is the territory it is controlling today."[2] This conclusion was drawn from an extensive report made by two prestigious military think tanks.

Pushed Toward 'Samson Option'

In the late 1970s, Israel agreed to give up the Sinai Peninsula to Egypt in exchange for a peace treaty. Many military and intelligence experts agree further land concessions would leave Israel indefensible borders with no conventional deterrent against attack.

Notice the word "conventional." This is because Israel still has its non-conventional form of deterrence—nuclear weapons. With these they have formed a last resort-battle-plan known as the "Samson Option." With the totally indefensible borders into which they are being pushed, Israel would be quickly forced into initiating this last resort. Is this what Western leaders want to do?

There is an appalling ignorance of the volatile Mid-East situation within our State Department. The current American President, George W. Bush, who is at heart a friend of Israel, is getting some very bad advise. He is also getting a lot of pressure from old friends and family in the oil business to "placate and appease" Arab oil barons. This has resulted in a misguided decision to push Israel into accepting a Palestinian state, that is, and will continue to be, run by the most vicious terrorists the world has seen.

---

2. *Intelligence Digest*, July 29, 1992.

ISRAEL'S HARD CHOICE

Israelis live in the toughest neighborhood of the world. It has no other option but to stand strong and hold on to its defensible borders. The citizens of Israel are weary of war; weary of seeing their sons and daughters killed in the prime of their youth. There has developed a "peace at any price" mentality in many. But Israelis have one option, stay tough and fight, or pack up and get out of the Middle East. It sounds harsh, but the facts back it up.

ISLAM WILL NEVER ACCEPT ISRAEL

The present territorial concessions Israel is being pressured into making have absolutely no chance of appeasing the Muslims. History shows clearly Israel will never be small enough for the Muslims. Their real quarrel with Israel has never been the size of its borders, but its existence.

In fact, Muslim nations don't care about the so-called "legitimate rights of the Palestinians"—or Jordan and Egypt would have given them a state when they controlled the territory they are now seeking from Israel. They would have helped the Palestinians out of the horrible refugee camps long ago. No, it's the destruction of the Jewish state they are after, and the Palestinians are being used as pawns for achieving that goal.

As I have sought repeatedly to point out, this is a blood feud that dates back to the tents of Abraham. A blood feud that became an integral part of Islam. The ancient hatred of Israel is now sanctified and nourished by the Koran and the Muslim religion.

ALLAH'S HONOR AT STAKE

Annihilating Israel and removing its occupation of Jerusalem has become an issue of "removing an insult to Allah's honor" for the devout Muslim.

"The rebirth of the Jewish state right in the midst of the Arab countries is a direct contradiction of Islamic teaching," explains author Elishua Davidson. "Has not Allah finished with the Jewish people?"[3] If Allah has predetermined all things, how is it possible that a Jewish state should have come into existence again?

Before his death, the Ayatollah Ruhollah Khomeini set Iran on a course of Islamic fundamentalism from which they have not deviated. They are determined to do Allah's will—destroy Israel and prove to the world its creation was merely a historical anomaly. Iran is primarily responsible for the worldwide revival of Islamic fundamentalism. And the so-called "moderate" leaders haven't changed the original direction of Khomeini's revolution one iota.

The Treaty From Hell

Despite the current "friendship" between President Bush and Russian President Vladimir Putin, a binding agreement between Iran and Russia is still in force. There are still hard-liners waiting in the wings for an opportune moment.

As briefly mentioned before, this treaty was formed and put into action in February of 1991 under the code name "the Grand Design". Russia was terrified of Iran spreading their Islamic fundamentalist revolution into the five former Soviet Union republics that are Muslim, and rightly so. The small state of Chechnya has demonstrated to the Russians how enormous a threat the five larger republics would pose if controlled by hostile foes.

So, an exchange was worked out. Iran promised neither to encourage fundamentalism or hostility toward Russia in the five states, nor to interfere with Russian "internal attempts" to quell Islamic terrorism whenever it appeared. Russia in exchange would do the following:

- Provide plants, equipment and expert personnel for the construction of nuclear warheads and missile delivery systems

---

3. Elishua Davidson, *Islam, Israel and the Last Days* (Eugene, OR: Harvest House Publishers, 1991) p. 92.

- Fight alongside Iran against the West in the event of an attack by Western forces.

In late February of 1991, 278 of Russia's top nuclear and missile experts moved to Isfahan, Iran and began helping Iran become a nuclear power. Today it appears they achieved their mission. Iran has now successfully tested a missile capable of accurately delivering a warhead on target 1600 miles away.

ISRAEL IN THE CROSSHAIRS

Israel is now within missile range, as well as some parts of Europe, yet Iran is determined to develop missiles that can hit the continental United States as well. When that happens, we are genuinely in trouble. A fundamental part of the Iranian conceived "Grand Design Strategy" is to block the U.S. from coming to Israel's aid while combined Muslim nations destroy it.

An Israeli intelligence officer made these developments known to me in April 1991. Until they became public knowledge, I could not speak about them.

For two years after this, I observed the amazingly accurate British *Intelligence Digest* warn about these secret alliances between Russia and Iran. The *Digest* revealed that because Russia recognizes it can't compete with the economic power of the West, they must link to the Third World where they can be the leader. This required them to make alliances with the radical Muslim powers on the basis of economic assistance for world-class military weapons and co-belligerence toward the west. It confirmed the information about Russia's fear of Islamic fundamentalism and Iran's agreement not to spread it into the former Soviet republics that are Muslim. The *Digest* said outright this meant, "The Russians would be compelled to fight alongside the Muslims in the next Arab-Israeli war."

The Digest continued,

Since the break up of the Soviet Union this service has

consistently argued that Russia will eventually return to its traditional role of heading up an anti-Western, predominantly Islamic, Third-World alliance.[4]

The motivating forces are various and complex, but of primary importance is its need to appease Iran. Only by making a strategic alliance with Iran, in which Moscow backs Tehran's southerly ambitions (i.e., the conquest against Saudi Arabia and Israel), can Russia ensure its own interests in Central Asia.

. . . We now have further information on the Russian-Iranian relationship – this time from sources in Riyadh. Saudi Arabia is, of course, one of the countries most threatened by a Russian-Iranian strategic alliance. This information was confirmed on 26 July (1993) by a report in the Saudi daily Asharq al-Awsat. According to this report, Russia and Iran are in the final stages of putting together a nuclear co-operation treaty under the terms of which Moscow will build two nuclear power plants, train nuclear technicians, and set up a nuclear research facility in Isfahan.[5]

8-16-06

Today, that work has been completed. If Iran does not have a nuclear arsenal already, they soon will. It's only a matter of time.

To those familiar with Bible prophecy, these events have familiar ring to them. Ezekiel predicted a power from the extreme north of the reborn Israeli state will arm and lead a confederacy of nations against Israel and western forces in the last days. The nations Ezekiel named are all Muslim today—and the first on the list is Persia or Iran.

The Deadly 'Quraysh Strategy'

Muslims have long been known for their "Quarysh Strategy." As history is said to repeat itself, a brief review can help us be more

---

4. *Intelligence Digest*, August, 1993.

5. Ibid.

aware of what will happen in the near future. Within a year after signing a ten-year peace treaty with the forces of Mecca, Mohammad had gathered enough forces to attack them. He then ignored the "peace treaty", annihilated the Quraysh custodians of Mecca and took it over. This became known in Muslim history as the Quraysh Model strategy. Yasser Arafat explained in a South African Mosque that his signing of the Oslo Peace Accord of 1993 was according to the "Quraysh Model."

The late Faisal Husseini, Arafat's Jerusalem representative, confirmed the "Quraysh Model" was indeed the strategy behind the Oslo Accords. Husseini was a cultured and sophisticated man. He was considered the "most moderate" of all the Palestinians. Yet, shortly before his death on May 31, 2001, he expressed his true feelings in an interview with the popular Egyptian newspaper *el Arav*. Husseini said: "We must distinguish the strategies and long-term goals from the political-phased goals which we are compelled to accept due to international pressures." But the *"ultimate goal is the liberation of all of historical Palestine."* He said explicitly: *"Oslo has to be viewed as a Trojan Horse."* He clarified that it is the obligation of all Palestinian forces and factions to see the Oslo Accords as "temporary" steps, as "gradual" goals, because in this way, "We are setting an ambush for the Israelis and cheating them."[6]

The United Nations, the European Union and, yes, even the United States, are pushing Israel to grant a Palestinian State. This is despite the fact that multiple terrorist organizations within the Palestinian territories will not halt terrorist attacks long enough for the Palestinian state to be negotiated and granted.

Ultimately, something will happen to the United States to neutralize us a major power. Then the predicted European leaders out of Rome will negotiate the final "peace treaty" between the Muslims and Israel. The signing of this treaty begins a seven-year count down to the return of Jesus the Messiah.

---

6. Sharon Nader Sloan & Beth Kennedy, *We Have Been Had*, Commentary in *Israel Insider*, May 27, 2002, emphasis added.

IT IS ALL PREDICTED

As incredible as it may sound to some readers, the precise scenario of how this will end was predicted over 2000 years ago. Everything happening today is fitting exactly into the forecasted pattern of events.

How it all ends is the subject of the next chapter.

CHAPTER FIFTEEN

Armageddon:
The Climax of Hate

"They say, 'Come, LET US WIPE THEM OUT AS A NATION; LET THE NAME OF ISRAEL BE REMEMBERED NO MORE.' They conspire with one accord; against You they make a covenant—the tents of Edom and the Ishmaelites (The Arabs), Moab and the Hagrites, Gebal and Ammon and Amalek (Jordan), Philistia with the inhabitants of Tyre (Lebanon); Assyria (Syria) also has joined them . . ."

PSALM 83:4-8, EMPHASIS ADDED

"The word of the LORD came to Jeremiah: "Have you not noticed that these people (Israel's neighboring nations) are saying, 'The

LORD *has rejected the two families he chose'? SO THEY DESPISE MY PEOPLE AND NO LONGER REGARD THEM AS A NATION."* 'This is what the LORD says: "If I have not established my covenant with day and night and the fixed laws of heaven and earth, then I will reject the descendants of Jacob and David my servant and will not choose one of his sons to rule over the descendants of Abraham, Isaac and Jacob. For I will bring them back from captivity and have compassion on them.'"

JEREMIAH 33:23-26, EMPHASIS ADDED

"I will lay waste your cities, and you will become a desolation. Then you will know that I am the Lord. BECAUSE YOU (the Arab people) HAVE HAD EVERLASTING ENMITY and have delivered the sons of Israel to the power of the sword at the time of their calamity, at the time of the punishment of the end-time, therefore, as I live," declares the LORD God, "I will give you over to bloodshed, and bloodshed will pursue you; since you have not hated bloodshed, therefore bloodshed will pursue you."

EZEKIEL 35:4-6, EMPHASIS ADDED

Overview of Prophetic Scenario

Beginning 3400 years ago and continuing into the next 1400 years, the Hebrew prophets predicted a precise sequence of events would fit together. All the elements of this predicted pattern would lead to a cataclysmic war of such magnitude that it will almost end life on this planet.

Even though different prophets at different times predicted the various components of these events, they can be easily identified and joined together because they pertain to the great, final conflict which begins in the Middle East and draws all nations into it. The scenario deals with circumstances leading to this war, the war itself and incidents that immediately follow.

Concerning this global catastrophe, known as the Battle of Armageddon, Jesus Christ predicted,

> **For then there will be great distress, unequaled from the beginning of the world until now—and never to be equaled again. If those days had not been cut short, no one would survive, but for the sake of the elect those days will be shortened.**[1]

The prophet Daniel foresaw this same war and also notes it will be without parallel:

> **There will be a time of distress such as has not happened from the beginning of nations until then. But at that time your people—everyone whose name is found written in the book—will be delivered.**[2]

The prophet Isaiah wrote about this bloodshed:

> **The earth will be completely laid waste and completely despoiled, for the Lord has spoken this word . . . The earth is also polluted by its inhabitants, for they transgressed laws, violated statutes, broke the everlasting covenant. Therefore, a curse devours the earth, and**

---

1. Matthew 24:21–22 (NIV).
2. Daniel 12:1 (NIV).

those who live in it are held guilty. Therefore, the inhab-itants of the earth are burned, and few men are left.[3]

Isaiah also points out that very few people will survive.

Knowing the General Time
ISRAEL REBORN

The key that would indicate the predicted scenario was begin-ning would be the miraculous return and national rebirth of the scattered Israelites to their ancient homeland. This was formally fulfilled May 15, 1948. As foretold, the ancient hatred of neigh-boring nations has contested Israel's existence from the beginning.

JERUSALEM RECAPTURED

Jesus Christ predicted how Jerusalem would fit into this prophetic timetable, **". . . and they** (Jews in A.D. 70) **will fall by the edge of the sword, and will be led captive into all the nations; and Jerusalem will be trampled under foot by the Gentiles UNTIL the times of the Gentiles be fulfilled."**[4] Jesus made this prophecy just before his death. He predicted the destruction and dispersion of the nation would fall upon the generation that reject-ed Him. His words came true 37 years later.

The second half of this prophecy *puts a time limit* on the period of Jerusalem's desolations and captivity. Jesus forewarned it would be only **"UNTIL the times of the Gentiles are fulfilled."** The "times of the Gentiles"—their world domination—began a final countdown in June of 1967 with Israel's recapture of old Jerusalem. This process will be completed with the coming of the Messiah to set up God's Kingdom.

---

3. Isaiah 24:3, 5–6.
4. Luke 21:24, emphasis added.

ISLAM'S JIHAD FOR JERUSALEM

Zechariah predicted,

> **Behold, I am going to make Jerusalem a cup that causes intoxication to all the surrounding peoples; and when the siege is against Jerusalem, it will also be against Judah** (the Jews). **And it will come about in that day that I will make Jerusalem a burdensome stone for all the peoples; all who attempt to lift it will be severely injured. And all the nations of the earth will be gathered** [for war] **because of it.**[5]

As prophesied, Israel has regained control of its ancient capitol city, Jerusalem, amid tremendous opposition from surrounding nations. Like the prophet Zechariah foresaw some 2450 years ago, Jerusalem will cause all of the neighboring nations (which are Muslim today) to become intoxicated with religious passion to possess it.

The metaphor, **"a cup that causes intoxication"** is used in the Bible to illustrate out of control religious passions. Just as a drunken person acts emotionally without reason, so it was predicted the neighboring states would be <u>intoxicated</u> <u>with religiously driven passion</u> and <u>hate.</u>

AL QUDS?

It is vital to recognize the name "Jerusalem" never appears in the Koran. The claim to this city arose years after Mohammad's death. The justification for this comes from a verse which says Mohammad traveled to the "uttermost mosque," (which is the meaning of *Al Quds* in Arabic) shortly before his death.

The legend that Mohammad, escorted by the angel Michael, flew on a winged horse named Barak to the Temple Mount in Jerusalem first appeared in the days of Khaliph Omar, the Muslim who originally conquered Jerusalem. As the story goes, Mohammad ascended to the seventh heaven from the great rock on top of the

---

5. Zechariah 12:2–3 (Literal translation from Hebrew).

Temple Mount. He then returned to the rock and flew back to Mecca.

Omar was the first to erect a Mosque over the sacred site. A more magnificent Mosque was later built there—the Dome of the Rock. No historical evidence shows that Mohammad was ever in Jerusalem. But in the Middle East, it doesn't matter whether something is actually true. What is believed to be true is all that matters. Many have died for the sake of myths.

JERUSALEM, THE BURDENSOME STONE

As predicted by Zechariah, Jerusalem has become a heavy burden to all people. It is at the heart of the Muslim fervor to demolish Israel, and is considered their third holiest place, on par with Mecca and Medina. They believe their sacred duty to Allah is to retake Jerusalem and Palestine.

Because the Muslims control most of the world's oil reserves, they can make their troubles the world's as well. This prophecy indicates Islam's religious obsession to capture Jerusalem and drive the Jews out the Middle East will ignite a global war, for it is written, **"all nations will gather for war because of Jerusalem."**

The Four Spheres of Gentile Power

The Last Days scenario features four spheres of political power. These power blocs become aligned during the general time of Israel's restoration and rebirth. The dispute over Jerusalem draws all into it, much like a whirlpool pulls in all around it.

① • There will be the Muslim sphere of power Daniel called "the king of the South."

② • There will be the Asian sphere of power designated "the kings of the East."

③ • There will be the power of the West known as the Revived Roman Empire.

• There will be the "King of the North" who comes from the extreme north of Israel.

·THE MUSLIM SPHERE OF POWER

Many prophets declared God's "Last Days" warning to the nations surrounding Israel. Great Judgment is predicted for these nations because God says, **"they appropriated My land and mistreated My people Israel."**[6]

When I wrote *The Late Great Planet Earth* in 1969, the Muslim nations were nothing like the threat they are now. Because of Bible prophecy, I recognized that with Russian help, Muslims had to be one of the power blocs of the Last Days.

Gamal Abdel Nasser of Egypt led the Islamic nations in the late 1960s. He sought to unite the Muslim world under a secular Arab Socialism. The Soviet Union was, at the same time, seeking to promote Islam's war against Israel in order to bring the Muslims under Communist control. But this was an unnatural relationship. Neither socialism nor communism agreed with the Koran.

IRAN'S IMPORTANCE

Ezekiel's prophecy named Persia as leader of the Muslim sphere of power for the final conflict, not Egypt. But at the time, the Shah was, next to Israel, the United States' best friend in the Middle East.

When the Shah of Iran was driven out and replaced by the Ayatollah Khomeini in 1979, a dramatic change in the Muslim world began to take place. The United States inexplicably withdrew its help and support for the Shah at a critical time. We have paid and will continue to pay a huge price for that, for Iran has now become the leader of the whole Muslim world, not through some secular political system, but through a return to the "pure fundamentals of the Koran." This is an almost irresistible appeal to the heart of a Muslim.

---

6. Ezekiel 36:5.

The Islamic fundamentalist revolution began and continues through Iran. This movement appeals to young Muslim men to sacrifice their lives for a heavenly reward of fleshly pleasures they can only dream of on earth. It has produced the most formidable terrorists in history, and has the potential of destroying the United States as a world power.

ISLAM WARNED BY JEHOVAH GOD

When Ezekiel predicted the miraculous Last Days restoration of the land of Israel, he also condemned the neighboring nations for confiscating God's land. Read how accurately the details of Ezekiel's prophecy fit the current situation in "Israel-Palestine,"

> **And you, son of man, prophesy to the mountains of Israel and say, "O mountains of Israel, hear the word of the Lord. Thus says the LORD God, 'Because the enemy has spoken against you, "Aha!" and, "The everlasting heights have become our possession" . . . Therefore, O mountains of Israel, hear the word of the LORD God. Thus says the LORD God to the mountains and to the hills, to the ravines and to the valleys, to the desolate wastes and to the forsaken cities, which have become a prey and a derision to the rest of the NATIONS WHICH ARE ROUND ABOUT . . . Surely in the fire of My jealousy I have spoken against the rest of the nations, and AGAINST ALL EDOM** (collective name for Arabs), **who appropriated My land for themselves as a possession with wholehearted joy and with scorn of soul, to drive it out for a prey . . . Therefore, thus says the LORD God, 'I have sworn that surely the NATIONS WHICH ARE AROUND YOU will themselves endure their insults. But you, O mountains of Israel, you will put forth your branches and bear your fruit for My people Israel; for they will soon come.'"**[7]

---

7. Ezekiel 36:1–8.

WHO OWNS THE LAND?

Who owns the land that the Romans, out of spite, renamed Philistia or Philistina after the ancient enemies of Israel—the Philistines? Arabs couldn't pronounce "Philistina", so it came to be called by its Arab pronunciation, "Palestine." In the prophecy just noted, God makes it clear Arabs don't own the land, and neither do Jews. He says it's **"My Land."**

The Lord expresses His fury at the Muslim nations for appropriating His land and desecrating it, reducing it to utter desolation. God declares that He will bring His people back, and that this land will flourish at their touch. In an earlier chapter, I stated God would return the land to the Israelites on the basis of His unconditional covenant with them, despite the fact they do not deserve it. The LORD explains this:

> **Therefore, say to the house of Israel, "Thus says the LORD God, 'It is not for your sake, O house of Israel, that I am about to act, but for My holy name, which you have profaned among the nations where you went . . . For I will take you from the nations, gather you from all the lands, and bring you into your own land.'"** [8]

When God makes a promise, His name is involved. He will not break a promise, no matter how unworthy the recipients may be. So, He sovereignly announces that He will cause a remnant to believe and be saved.

THE POWER FROM THE EXTREME NORTH

In the same general timeframe, Ezekiel predicts the rise of another key piece of the prophetic pattern. There are several major Biblical predictions about this northern player found in Ezekiel 38 and 39; Daniel 11:40–45; and Joel 2:20. Ezekiel gives three clues with which to identify this power.

First, a *geographic* clue. This attacking nation will come against

---

8. Ezekiel 36:22, 24.

Israel from "the uttermost or extreme north." This information is repeated three times. Ezekiel predicts the invader will come:

> . . . from the remote parts of the north with all its troops —many peoples with you.[9]

> And you will come from your piace out of the remote parts of the north, you and many peoples with . . .[10]

> I shall turn you around, drive you on, take you from the remotest parts of the north, and bring you against the mountains of Israel.[11]

The Hebrew word translated **"remote parts of the north"** literally means "extreme north."

There is only one country that covers the great expanse to the north of the Middle East and Asia. Take a globe and look to the extreme north from Israel, and you'll find only one nation there—Russia.

Second, a _time clue_. Ezekiel clearly identifies when this nation would rise to power:

> After many days you will be summoned; in the latter years you will come into the land that is restored from the sword, whose inhabitants have been gathered from many nations to the mountains of Israel which had been a continual waste; but its people were brought out from the nations, and they are living securely, all of them.

Ezekiel says this hostile country will fight against Israel after the Jews have been brought back from their worldwide dispersion and reunited in "the latter year." That time is now—the nation of Israel has been reborn.

Third, a _ethnic clue_. Ezekiel writes that this northern power is descended from the ancient tribes of Magog, Meshech and Tubal.

---

9. Ezekiel 38:6.

10. Ezekiel 38:15.

11. Ezekiel 39:2.

All of these groups spread north of the Caucasus Mountains at the dawn of recorded history.

Fifth century B.C. Greek historian Herodotus is quoted as mentioning Meshech and Tubal. He identified them as the Samaritans and Muschovites who lived, at that time, north of Asia Minor.[12]

Josephus, a Jewish historian of the first century, says the people of his day, known as the Moschevi and Thobelites, were founded by Meshech and Tubal respectively. He also said, ". . . Magog is called the Scythians by the Greeks." He reported that these people lived in the northern regions above the Caucasus Mountains.[11]

These fierce tribes became known collectively as the Scythians. Scythians are easily traced in history as the principle forefathers of modern ethnic Russians.

Russia is not predicted as a world conqueror, but rather a dangerous regional power with vast arsenals of deadly weapons. They will lead a confederacy of nations, which today are all Muslim, equipping them with weapons.[14]

Persia, or Iran is the first confederate named.[15] It is no coincident they have signed a treaty with Russia binding it to fight alongside the Iranians if the West attacks. Russia has supplied the Muslim nations with the most lethal weapons known to man.

The last war will begin with a coordinated attack against Israel by the Iranian led Muslim forces joined by Russia.

---

12. Walter Chamberlain, *The National Resources and Conversion of Israel* (London, 1854).

13. Louis Bauman, *Russian Events in the Light of Bible Prophecy* (Philadelphia: The Balkiston Co., 1952)

14. See Ezekiel 38:5–6. **Persia** is Iran; **Put** (Hebrew word erroneously translated Libya) is forefather of the Muslim North African people of Libya, Algeria, Tunisia, Morocco, Mauritania; **Cush** (Hebrew for Ethiopia) is the forefather of all black African people; **Gomer** is thought to be a forefather of various Balkan and European peoples; **Togarmah**, a son of Gomer, is the forefather of the Turkic peoples such as Turkey, Turkmenistan, Uzbekistan, Kyrgyzstan, Kazakhstan, Tajikistan and Afghanistan. Most important is that all are Muslims today.

15. Ezekiel 38:5.

THE ASIAN CONFEDERATION

During this same era, the book of Revelation records the rise of an enormous power in Asia. The Apostle John writes of **"the kings of the East"** [16] who come from east of the Euphrates River. In his day, that was the dividing line between the Near East and the Far East. This Asian confederacy will cross the Euphrates River with 200 million soldiers after the Russian-Muslim attack is launched.

I believe China is destined to lead this Asian confederation. When John made the cryptic prophecy of a vast 200-million-man army,[17] there were not that many people in the world. This sphere of power will kill a third of mankind. The Apostle John's account of the phenomena that annihilates this unprecedented number of people is a good first century description of the effects of a modern thermonuclear war. Just imagine this prophecy's fulfillment in terms of today's population. That number translates into two billion people, killed in a matter of days. No wonder both Jesus and Daniel said, **"For then there will be great distress, unequaled from the beginning of the world until now—and never to be equaled again."** [18]

THE GROWING POWER OF ASIA

China, North Korea and India already have nuclear weapons and systems to deliver them. They are rapidly improving their technology and enlarging their arsenals. Watch for China to move toward establishing hegemony over Asian nations such as the Koreas, Japan, India and Southeast Asia. On the basis of prophecy, these nations are destined to join together, both economically and militarily.

It is easy to see why any attempt to take over the Middle East's

---

16. Revelation 16:12–16.
17. Revelation 9:14–16.
18. Daniel 12:1–2 and Matthew 24:21–22.

strategic land bridge and the region's oil reserves would be immediately countered by an Asian attack.

The Western Sphere Of Power

Ultimately, the western sphere of power will take over all others for a short period. It is predicted more often and in greater detail than all others powers. It will be a revived form of the old Roman Empire, its capitol being Rome.

We can have great confidence in this prophecy's fulfillment. Four-fifths of it has already dramatically taken place. Daniel predicted four successive empires that would gain authority over the whole world from God's perspective.

In Daniel 2, 7 and 8, the prophet predicted the details of these empires. The first was Babylonian; the second, Media-Persia; and the third, Greek. Even Alexander the Great and his four successors were graphically predicted.[19] Considering that Daniel wrote this chapter in around 539 B.C., it is awesome.

In 68 B.C., the fourth empire, Rome, conquered the remains of the Greek empire. It became the mightiest and longest lasting of all the others. The prophets did not forecast the fourth empire would be conquered or utterly destroyed, but rather that it would become dormant. It would rise again shortly before the coming of the Messiah. Daniel specifically predicts, **". . . OUT OF this kingdom ten kings will arise, and another will arise after them he will be different from the previous ones and will subdue three kings."**

Daniel says it is **"out of"** the culture and people of the old Roman Empire that the ten nations will come. While it does not say this confederation will be geographically coextensive with the old, one specific part of the old remains the same—Rome must be the capitol. The Book of Revelation predicts this with the symbol

---

19. See Daniel 8:20–22. The first King of Greece was Alexander the Great. The "four horns" that took over his Empire at his death were Lysimicus, Seleucus, Cassander and Ptolemy.

of **"a woman. And the woman whom you saw is the great city, which reigns over the kings of the earth."** [20] When the Apostle John wrote this, there was only one city reigning over the kings of the earth—Rome.

ROME'S COMING LEADER

Daniel and John both announced a revival of the Roman Empire will happen through the genius and supernatural power of a great leader. He will come from Rome, for Daniel says he will be out of the people who destroyed Jerusalem and Israel in A.D. 70. [21]

John proclaims the ten nations will not receive power until this leader (called "the beast") arrives to pull them together:

> **And the ten horns which you saw are ten kings, who have not yet received a kingdom, but they receive authority as kings with the beast for one hour. These have one purpose and they give their power and authority to the beast.** [22]

In 1969, I said the European Common Market would become the United States of Europe. [23] Most critics said this would never happen. In fact, one Cardinal in Rome branded me a "false prophet" for it. But today, we have what Charlemagne, Napoleon, Hitler and many others could not accomplish—the European Union (EU).

I believe this final Roman leader is alive somewhere in Europe right now, waiting for his appointed time. He is the one who will take ten of the strongest nations in the EU and form them into a power base with which he will gain control over the whole world.

---

20. Revelation 17:18. The Greek verb is present tense, which literally means, "is reigning".

21. See Daniel 9:26 where it predicts "the Prince that shall come" will be from the people who destroy the city (Jerusalem) and the sanctuary (the Temple), which happened in A.D. 70 with Titus of Rome and the Roman Tenth Legion.

22. Revelation 17:12–13.

23. Hal Lindsey, *The Late Great Planet Earth* (Grand Rapids, MI: Zondervan Publishing, 1970), pp. 94–97.

John predicts he will use a religious system to help bring the world under his authority. This man is called by many titles in the Bible, but the best known is "the Antichrist."

The Antichrist will declare war on all who believe in Jesus Christ, and he will be worshiped and followed by the entire world:

> **And it was given to him to make war with the saints and to overcome them; and authority over every tribe and people and tongue and nation was given to him. And all who dwell on the earth will worship him, everyone whose name has not been written from the foundation of the world in the book of life of the Lamb who has been slain.**[24]

Apparently two events will thrust the Antichrist into world prominence. First, he will receive a mortal wound from which he will miraculously recover.[25] Second, he will settle the Arab-Israeli conflict by making a covenant with Israel guaranteeing their security.[26] This will usher in what appears to be a new era of peace, and freedom from fear of war. Israel will even be able to rebuild their Temple next to the Dome of the Rock mosque. The joy they'll experience is evident in their praise: **"And they worshiped the dragon (Satan), because he gave his authority to the beast (Antichrist); and they worshiped the beast, saying, 'Who is like the beast, and who is able to wage war with him.'"**[27]

Events that Trigger Armageddon

A worldwide euphoria will exist in the pseudo-peace the Antichrist brings, continuing for three-and-a-half years. Then, the Antichrist will enter the Holy of Holies in Israel's rebuilt Temple, take a seat there and proclaim himself god.[28] This is the desecra-

---

24. Revelation 13:7–8.
25. Revelation 13:3–4.
26. Daniel 9:27.
27. Revelation 13:4.
28. 2 Thessalonians 2:3–4.

tion of the Temple known as **"the abomination that causes desolation"** spoken of by Daniel and Jesus Christ.

At this point, all hell breaks loose. Jesus warned this is the sign that the great war of Armageddon is starting.[29]

DANIEL'S PREVIEW OF ARMAGEDDON'S BATTLE PLAN

Daniel traces the movement of the military forces in the last great conflict:

> **At the time of the end the king of the South** (Muslim forces) **will engage him** (the Antichrist) **in battle, and the king of the North** (Russia) **will storm out against him with chariots and cavalry and a great fleet of ships. He will invade many countries and sweep through them like a flood. He will also invade the Beautiful Land** (Israel). **Many countries will fall, but Edom, Moab and the leaders of Ammon** (Jordan) **will be delivered from his hand. He will extend his power over many countries; Egypt will not escape. He will gain control of the treasures of gold and silver and all the riches of Egypt, with the Libyans** (North Africans) **and Nubians** (Black Africans) **in submission. But reports from the east** (Asian Invasion) **and the north** (Western Forces) **will alarm him, and he will set out in a great rage to destroy and annihilate many. He will pitch his royal tents between the seas at the beautiful holy mountain** (Jerusalem). **Yet he will come to his end, and no one will help him.**[30]

The initial attack is launched against Israel by the Arab Muslim confederacy. "Him" refers to the Roman Antichrist and his partner known as the False Prophet[31] from Israel. (See description of "him" in Daniel 11:36–39.)

---

29. Matthew 24:15–22.

30.

31. He is the second beast of Revelation 13:11–18.

The Muslims are immediately joined by the Russians in an all out assault on Israel. But then the Russian leader also invades Egypt and Africa. While in Egypt, troubling reports come from the *east*, which would concern the oncoming Asian army, and from *north* of Egypt, telling of the European led Western army.

The Russian leader retraces his steps to make a stand in Jerusalem. There the Roman led Western armies of the Antichrist annihilate both the Russian and Muslim armies.

Following this, the 200 million-man army of Asia will square off against the Western forces along the length and breadth of the Middle East, with its vortex in the valley of Megiddo. It is at this point John foresaw a horrible vision of **"blood standing to the horses' bridle for a distance of 200 miles."** [32] He indicates the blood primarily flows from around Jerusalem. The 200-mile Jordan River rift valley stretches from north of the Sea of Galilee to the Red Sea at Aqaba-Eilat.

Ezekiel wrote the war would escalate into the rest of the world, **"I will send fire on Magog and on those who live in safety in the coastlands, and they will know that I am the LORD."** [33] The Hebrew word translated "coastlands" means continents today. Apparently the fire of thermonuclear weapons will reach most of the world.

As man is about to destroy all life on the planet, Jesus the Messiah will return to conquer all armies. He will then judge the world, casting off all unbelievers into judgment. The faithful who survive will repopulate a completely renewed earth and live in peace and prosperity for a thousand years.

WHAT ABOUT THE UNITED STATES?

This question has troubled me for the 40 odd years I have studied prophecy. I have not found one reference, either explicit or

32. Revelation 14:20.
33. Ezekiel 39:6 (NIV).

inferred, listing the United States in the final alignment of world powers. Since the U.S. has been the leader of the west and the world since World War II, this has an ominous meaning.

The power that will head the West is clearly predicted. It will be a Roman-led alliance of the ten strongest nations of the European Union. So this means the U.S. must decline from power. I hate to even think this because I love my country. But frankly, since 9/11 I can see the potential of terrorist attacks, causing us to diminish as a major power.

However it happens, control must shift to Europe. Prophecy demands it.

NOW SOME GOOD NEWS

The good news is those who accept the free gift of pardon, that Jesus gave His life to purchase, will not be here in the fateful, final seven years of catastrophe.

I was a young tugboat captain in New Orleans, satisfied with life. I thought I had everything—a bachelor's pad in the French Quarter and money to party non-stop. But after frantically indulging in all I thought was fun, I found myself asking, "Is this all there is?" "What do I do for an encore?" I started searching for meaning and eventually opened a Gideon's New Testament someone had given me years before. I had never read it, but thought it was "good luck" to keep with me.

In the third chapter of the Gospel of John it suddenly became clear to me I had been born sinful the first time, and I needed to be born again spiritually. I saw that the only requirement was to admit I could never measure up to God's standards. Then I simply asked God to forgive me on the basis that Jesus died for my sins and I received the pardon He purchased for me.

I didn't suddenly hear organ music or bells ringing, but I sensed a peace come over me. I knew God had touched me. It became the turning point in my whole life. Though I have had my struggles and failures, God has never let go of me. He has motivated me to learn His word and fellowship with other believers. I wouldn't trade the life I've had since that day for all the world has to offer.

The wonderful thing is, God promises all who believe in Him now are not appointed to the wrath that is about to come upon the world. I can't offer a solution for the world's problems, but I can offer a personal solution. Right now, wherever you are, just bow your head and receive the gift of pardon Jesus purchased for you by dying in your place.

May you find peace as I found it. I hope to see you at the great reunion.

[handwritten note]

Transcription of the original handwritten note:

If the Arabs are established as I have asked in my manifesto of Jan. 4, to the British Secretary of State Foreign Affairs, I will carry out what is within this agreement.

If changes are made I can not be answerable for failing to carry out this agreement.

Feisal ibn-Hussein

APPENDIX B

His Royal Highness the Emir FEISAL, representing
and acting on behalf of the Arab Kingdom of Hedjaz,
and Dr. CHAIM WEIZMANN, representing and acting on
behalf of the Zionist Organisation,

mindful of the racial kinship and ancient bonds existing between the Arabs and the Jewish people, and
realising that the surest means of working out the
consummation of their national aspirations, is through
the closest possible collaboration in the development
of the Arab State and Palestine, and being desirous
further of confirming the good understanding which
exists between them,

have agreed upon the following Articles;-

ARTICLE I.

The Arab State and Palestine in all their relations
and understakings shall be controlled by the most
cordial goodwill and understanding and to this end Arab

247

and Jewish duly accredited agents shall be established
and maintained in the respective territories.

ARTICLE II.

Immediately following the completion of the
deliberations of the Peace Conference, the definite
boundaries between the Arab State and Palestine shall
be determined by a Commission to be agreed upon by
the parties hereto.

ARTICLE III.

In the establishment of the Constitution and
Administration of Palestine all such measures shall
be adopted as will afford the fullest guarantees
for carrying into effect the British Government's
Declaration of the 2nd of November, 1917.

ARTICLE IV.

All necessary measures shall be taken to
encourage and stimulate immigration of Jews into
Palestine on a large scale, and as quickly as possible to settle Jewish immigrants upon the land
through closer settlement and intensive cultivation

of the soil. In taking such measures the Arab peasant and tenant farmers shall be protected in their rights, and shall be assisted in forwarding their economic development.

ARTICLE V.

No regulation nor law shall be made prohibiting or interfering in any way with the free exercise of religion; and further the free exercise and enjoyment of religious profession and worship without discrimination or preference shall forever be allowed. No religious test shall ever be required for the exercise of civil or political rights.

ARTICLE VI.

The Mohammedan Holy Places shall be under Mohammedan control.

ARTICLE VII.

The Zionist Organisation proposes to send to Palestine a Commission of experts to make a survey of the economic possibilities of the country, and to report upon the best means for its development. The Zionist Organisation will place the aforementioned Commission at the disposal of the Arab State for the purpose of a survey of the economic possibilities of the Arab State and to report upon the best means for its development. The Zienist Organisation will use its best efforts to assist the Arab State in providing the means for developing the natural resources and economic possibilities thereof.

ARTICLE VIII.

The parties hereto agree to act in complete accord and harmony on all matters embraced herein before the Peace Congress.

ARTICLE IX.

Any matters of dispute which may arise between the contracting parties shall be referred to the British Government for arbitration.

Given under our hand at LONDON, ENGLAND, the THIRD day of JANUARY, ONE THOUSAND NINE HUNDRED AND NINETEEN.

Chaim Weizmann

APPENDIX C

The San Remo Conference, 1922

(Extract)[1]

"The San Remo Conference decided on April 24, 1920 to assign the Mandate [for Palestine] under the League of Nations to Britain. The terms of the Mandate were also discussed with the United States, which was not a member of the League. An agreed text was confirmed by the Council of the League of Nations on July 24, 1922, and it came into operation in September 1923."

---

1. From *The Israel-Arab Reader*, edited, Walter Laqueur, New York, Bantam Books, 1976, pp 34–42. [NB: This is an edited version of the complete San Remo Agreement, and the ellipses found within form part of Dr. Laqueur's editorial process.]

The Council of the League of Nations

Whereas the Principal Allied Powers have agreed, for the purpose of giving effect to the provisions of Article 22 of the Covenant of the League of Nations, to entrust to a Mandatory selected by the said Powers the administration of the territory of Palestine, which formerly belonged to the Turkish Empire, within such boundaries as may be fixed by them; and

Whereas the Principal Allied Powers have also agreed that the Mandatory should be responsible for putting into effect the declaration originally made on November 2nd, 1917, by the Government of His Britannic Majesty, and adopted by the said Powers, in favour of the establishment in Palestine of a national home for the Jewish people, it being clearly understood that nothing should be done which might prejudice the civil and religious rights of existing non-Jewish communities in Palestine, or the rights and political status enjoyed by Jews in any other country;

and

Whereas recognition has thereby been given to the historical connexion of the Jewish people with Palestine and to the grounds for reconstituting their national home in that country;

and

Whereas the Principal Allied Powers have selected His Britannic Majesty as the Mandatory for Palestine; and

Whereas the mandate in respect of Palestine has been formulated in the following terms and submitted to the Council of the League for approval; and

Whereas His Britannic Majesty has accepted the mandate in respect of Palestine and undertaken to exercise it on behalf of the League of Nations in conformity with the following provisions; and

Whereas by the aforementioned Article 22 (paragraph 8), it is provided that the degree of authority, control or administration to be exercised by the Mandatory, not having been previously agreed upon by the Members of the League, shall be explicitly defined by the Council of the League of Nations;

Confirming the said Mandate, defines its terms as follows:

ARTICLE 1

The Mandatory shall have full powers of legislation and of administration, save as they may be limited by the terms of this mandate.

ARTICLE 2

The Mandatory shall be responsible for placing the country under such political, administrative and economic conditions as will secure the establishment of the Jewish national home, as laid down in the preamble, and the development of self-governing institutions, and also for safeguarding the civil and religious rights of all the inhabitants of Palestine, irrespective of race and religion.

ARTICLE 3

The Mandatory shall, so far as circumstances permit, encourage local autonomy.

ARTICLE 4

An appropriate Jewish agency shall be recognized as a public body for the purpose of advising and cooperating with the Administration of Palestine in such economic, social and other matters as may affect the establishment of the Jewish national home and the interests of the Jewish population in Palestine, and, subject always to the control of the Administration, to assist and take part in the development of the country.

The Zionist Organization, so long as its organization and constitution are in the opinion of the Mandatory appropriate shall be recognized as such agency. It shall take steps in consultation with

His Britannic Majesty's Government to secure the cooperation of all Jews who are willing to assist in the establishment of the Jewish national home.

ARTICLE 5

The Mandatory shall be responsible for seeing that no Palestine territory shall be ceded or leased to, or in any way placed under the control of, the Government of any foreign Power.

ARTICLE 6

The Administration of Palestine, while ensuring that the rights and position of other sections of the population are not prejudiced, shall facilitate Jewish immigration under suitable conditions and shall encourage, in co-operation with the Jewish agency referred to in Article 4, close settlement by Jews on the land, including State lands and waste lands not required for public purposes.

ARTICLE 7

The Administration of Palestine shall be responsible for enacting a nationality law. There shall be included in this law provisions framed so as to facilitate the acquisition of Palestinian citizenship by Jews who take up their permanent residence in Palestine.

ARTICLE 8

The privileges and immunities of foreigners, including the benefits of consular jurisdiction and protection as formerly enjoyed by Capitulation or usage in the Ottoman Empire, shall not be applicable in Palestine.

Unless the Powers whose nationals enjoyed the aforementioned privileges and immunities on August 1st, 1914, shall have previously renounced the right to their re-establishment, or shall have agreed to their non-application for a specified period, these privileges and immunities shall, at the expiration of the mandate, be immediately re-established in their entirety or with such modifications as may have been agreed upon between the Powers concerned.

ARTICLE 9

The Mandatory shall be responsible for seeing that the judicial system established in Palestine shall assure to foreigners, as well as to natives, a complete guarantee of their rights.

Respect for the personal status of the various peoples and communities and for their religious interests shall be fully guaranteed. In particular, the control and administration of Waqfs shall be exercised in accordance with religious law and the dispositions of the founders.

ARTICLE 10

Pending the making of special extradition agreements relating to Palestine, the extradition treaties in force between the Mandatory and other foreign Powers shall apply to Palestine.

ARTICLE 11

The Administration of Palestine shall take all necessary measures to safeguard the interests of the community in connection with the development of the country, and, subject to any international obligations accepted by the Mandatory, shall have full power to provide for public ownership or control of any of the natural resources of the country or of the public works, services and utilities established or to be established therein. It shall introduce a land system appropriate to the needs of the country having regard, among other things, to the desirability of promoting the close settlement and intensive cultivation of the land.

The Administration may arrange with the Jewish agency mentioned in Article 4 to construct or operate, upon fair and equitable terms, any public works, services and utilities, and to develop any of the natural resources of the country, in so far as these matters are not directly undertaken by the Administration. Any such arrangements shall provide that no profits distributed by such agency, directly or indirectly, shall exceed a reasonable rate of interest on the capital, and any further profits shall be utilized by it for the benefit of the country in a manner approved by the Administration.

ARTICLE 12

The Mandatory shall be entrusted with the control of the foreign relations of Palestine, and the right to issue exequaturs to consuls appointed by foreign Powers. He shall also be entitled to afford diplomatic and consular protection to citizens of Palestine when outside its territorial limits.

ARTICLE 13

All responsibility in connexion with the Holy Places and religious buildings or sites in Palestine, including that of preserving existing rights and of securing free access to the Holy Places, religious buildings and sites and the free exercise of worship, while ensuring the requirements of public order and decorum, is assumed by the Mandatory, who shall be responsible solely to the League of Nations in all matters connected herewith, provided that nothing in this article shall prevent the Mandatory from entering into such arrangements as he may deem reasonable with the Administration for the purpose of carrying the provisions of this article into effect; and provided also that nothing in this Mandate shall be construed as conferring upon the Mandatory authority to interfere with the fabric or the management of purely Moslem sacred shrines, the immunities of which are guaranteed.

ARTICLE 14

A special Commission shall be appointed by the Mandatory to study, define and determine the rights and claims in connection with the Holy Places and the rights and claims relating to the different religious communities in Palestine. The method of nomination, the composition and the functions of this Commission shall be submitted to the Council of the League for its approval, and the Commission shall not be appointed or enter upon its functions without the approval of the Council.

ARTICLE 15

The Mandatory shall see that complete freedom of conscience and the free exercise of all forms of worship, subject only to the maintenance of public order and morals are ensured to all. No discrimination of any kind shall be made between the inhabitants of Palestine on the ground of race, religion or language. No person shall be excluded from Palestine on the sole ground of his religious belief.

The right of each community to maintain its own schools for the education of its own members in its own language, while conforming to such educational requirements of a general nature as the Administration may impose, shall not be denied or impaired.

ARTICLE 16

The Mandatory shall be responsible for exercising such supervision over religious or eleemosynary bodies of all faiths in Palestine as may be required for the maintenance of public order and good government. Subject to such supervision, no measures shall be taken in Palestine to obstruct or interfere with the enterprise of such bodies or to discriminate against any representative or member of them on the ground of his religion or nationality.

ARTICLE 17

The Administration of Palestine may organize on a voluntary basis the forces necessary for the preservation of peace and order, and also for the defense of the country, subject however, to the supervision of the Mandatory, but shall not use them for purposes other than those above specified save with the consent of the

Mandatory. Except for such purposes no military, naval or air forces shall be raised or maintained by the Administration of Palestine.

Nothing in this article shall preclude the Administration of Palestine from contributing to the cost of the maintenance of the forces of the Mandatory in Palestine.

The Mandatory shall be entitled at all times to use the roads, railways and ports of Palestine for the movement of armed forces and the carriage of fuel and supplies.

ARTICLE 18

The Mandatory shall see that there is no discrimination in Palestine against the nationals of any State Member of the League of Nations (including companies incorporated under its laws) as compared with those of the Mandatory or of any foreign State in matters concerning taxation, commerce or navigation, the exercise of industries or professions, or in the treatment of merchant vessels or civil aircraft. Similarly, there shall be no discrimination in Palestine against goods originating in or destined for any of the said States, and there shall be freedom of transit under equitable conditions across the mandated area.

Subject as aforesaid and to the other provisions of this mandate, the Administration of Palestine may, on the advice of the Mandatory, impose such taxes and customs duties as it may consider necessary, and take such steps as it may think best to promote the development of the natural resources of the country and to safeguard the interests of the population. It may also, on the advice of the Mandatory, conclude a special customs agreement with any State the territory of which in 1914 was wholly included in Asiatic Turkey or Arabia.

ARTICLE 19

The Mandatory shall adhere on behalf of the Administration of Palestine to any general international conventions already existing, or which may be concluded hereafter with the approval of the League of Nations, respecting the slave traffic, the traffic in arms and ammunition, or the traffic in drugs, or relating to commercial equality, freedom of transit and navigation, aerial navigation and postal, telegraphic and wireless communication or literary, artistic or industrial property.

ARTICLE 20

The Mandatory shall co-operate on behalf of the Administration of Palestine, so far as religious, social and other conditions may permit, in the execution of any common policy adopted by the League of Nations for preventing and combating disease, including diseases of plants and animals.

ARTICLE 21

The Mandatory shall secure the enactment within twelve months from this date, and shall ensure the execution of a Law of Antiquities based on the following rules. This law shall ensure equality of treatment in the matter of excavations and archaeological research to the nationals of all States Members of the League of Nations. . . .

ARTICLE 22

English, Arabic and Hebrew shall be the official languages of Palestine. Any statement or inscription in Arabic on stamps or money in Palestine shall be repeated in Hebrew and any statement or inscription in Hebrew shall be repeated in Arabic.

ARTICLE 23

The Administration of Palestine shall recognize the holy days of the respective communities in Palestine as legal days of rest for the members of such communities.

ARTICLE 24

The Mandatory shall make to the Council of the League of Nations an annual report to the satisfaction of the Council as to the measures taken during the year to carry out the provisions of the mandate. Copies of all laws and regulations promulgated or issued during the year shall be communicated with the report.

ARTICLE 25

In the territories Iying between the Jordan and the eastern boundary of Palestine as ultimately determined, the Mandatory shall be entitled, with the consent of the Council of the League of Nations, to postpone or withhold application of such provisions of this mandate as he may consider inapplicable to the existing local conditions, and to make such provision for the administration of the territories as he may consider suitable to those conditions, provided that no action shall be taken which is inconsistent with the provisions of Articles 15, 16 and 18.

ARTICLE 26

The Mandatory agrees that if any dispute whatever should arise between the Mandatory and another Member of the League of Nations relating to the interpretation or the application of the provisions of the mandate, such dispute, if it cannot be settled by negotiation, shall be submitted to the Permanent Court of International Justice provided for by Article 14 of the Covenant of the League of Nations.

ARTICLE 27

The consent of the Council of the League of Nations is required for any modification of the terms of this mandate.

ARTICLE 28

In the event of the termination of the mandate hereby conferred upon the Mandatory, the Council of the League of Nations shall make such arrangements as may be deemed necessary for safeguarding in perpetuity, under guarantee of the League, the rights secured by Articles 13 and 14, and shall use its influence for securing, under the guarantee of the League, that the Government of Palestine will fully honour the financial obligations legitimately incurred by the Administration of Palestine during the period of the mandate, including the rights of public servants to pensions or gratuities.

The present instrument shall be deposited in original in the archives of the League of Nations and certified copies shall be forwarded by the Secretary General of the League of Nations to all Members of the League.

DONE AT LONDON the twenty-fourth day of July, one thousand nine hundred and twenty-two.

APPENDIX D

The U.N. Partition Plan, 1947

The Armistice Demarcation Lines, 1949

Arab Population When Each Became a State after the Fall of Ottoman Empire

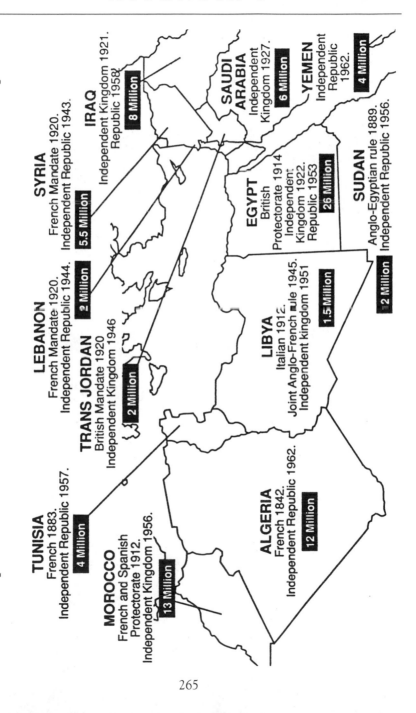

IRAQ
Independent Kingdom 1921.
Republic 1958.
8 Million

SAUDI ARABIA
Independent Kingdom 1927.
6 Million

YEMEN
Independent Republic 1962.
4 Million

SYRIA
French Mandate 1920.
Independent Republic 1943.
5.5 Million

EGYPT
British Protectorate 1914
Independent Kingdom 1922.
Republic 1953
26 Million

SUDAN
Anglo-Egyptian rule 1889.
Independent Republic 1956.
2 Million

LEBANON
French Mandate 1920.
Independent Republic 1944.
2 Million

TRANS JORDAN
British Mandate 1920
Independent Kingdom 1946
2 Million

LIBYA
Italian 1912.
Joint Anglo-French rule 1945.
Independent kingdom 1951
1.5 Million

TUNISIA
French 1883.
Independent Republic 1957.
4 Million

ALGERIA
French 1842.
Independent Republic 1962.
12 Million

MOROCCO
French and Spanish Protectorate 1912.
Independent Kingdom 1956.
13 Million

ABOUT THE AUTHOR

Hal Lindsey, named the best-selling author of the decade by the New York Times, was born in Houston, Texas. His first book, The Late Great Planet Earth, published in 1970, became the best-selling nonfiction book of that decade. As of this date, he has written 20 books with a total sales of more than 35 million copies worldwide. He is one of the few authors to have three books on the New York Times bestseller list at the same time.

Mr. Lindsey was educated at the University of Houston. He served in the U.S. Coast Guard during the Korean War. After the service, he served as a tugboat captain on the Mississippi River. During this time Hal came to a personal faith in Christ through reading a Gideon's New Testament. Several years later, Mr. Lindsey graduated from Dallas Theological Seminary where he majored in the New Testament and early Greek literature. After completing this graduate school of theology, Mr. Lindsey served for nine years on the staff of Campus Crusade for Christ, speaking to tens of thousands of students on major university campuses throughout the United States, Canada, and Mexico.

He presently travels to speak at conferences all over the world. He continues to write books, produce videos, audio tapes and CDs.

He also anchors a weekly television news show called the International Intelligence Briefing on KTBN which is viewed around the world.

Want to know more?

Do you want to learn how prophecy is being fulfilled on a day-to-day basis? Then visit Hal Lindsey's Oracle online at **www.hallindsey.com**. Updated daily with the help of Jack Kinsella, The Oracle not only examines current world events but keeps visitors abreast with Hal Lindsey's television and radio appearances, his latest releases and provides visitors with a secure online store.

Would you like Hal Lindsey to come and give a spiritual discourse for your organization or community? **Call 1-800-TITUS 35** to book speaking engagements and receive more information.

Did you know that Hal Lindsey has an plethora of faith strengthening materials to help faithful Christians through these last days? **Call 1-800-TITUS 35 for a free catalog** of books, compact discs, tapes, and videos to help you maintain your spiritual armor. Or, turn the page to view a few selections from Oracle House's catalog of spiritually enriching materials available now.

MIDDLE EAST: READY FOR WAR

Never before in history have so many unstable nations been armed with such weapons of mass destruction. Driven by the violent passions of Islam against Israel and Western Culture, The Muslim Nations of the Middle East have become bent on war. Islamic Fundamentalism has inflamed the Muslims of the world with the spirit of the "Jihad."

See how the "profit driven" nations like China, Russia, North Korea, France, Germany, etc., continue to sell weapons of mass destruction to "the Islamic War Machine."

In this latest powerful video, Hal Lindsey will show how all of this is fitting precisely into the predicted pattern for the "Last Days." Available on VHS and DVD. Please specify format when ordering.

Video ISBN 1-931628-13-0 . . . .$21.99 plus S/H
DVD ISBN 1-931628-14-9 . . . .$21.99 plus S/H

MYTHS OF THE MIDDLE EAST: DISPELLING THE LIES

No issue is more important to the world's future than the conflict between the Muslim world and the State of Israel. According to Bible prophecy, this conflict will drag the whole world into a final great war—a war that will almost destroy the planet and trigger the Second Coming of Christ. This video will expose the almost unbelievable myths on which this conflict is based. Such issues as: What impact did the Ottoman Turkish Empire have on the Middle East during its 400 year reign? Who lived in the Palestine Province at the end of the 19th century? Who is a Palestinian? Was there ever a Palestinian State? What land was originally given to the Jews by the League of Nations? and Who has the most valid claim to Jerusalem? The answers to these questions will shock you. Available on VHS. Please specify format when ordering.

Video ISBN 1-931628-10-6 . . . .$19.99 plus S/H

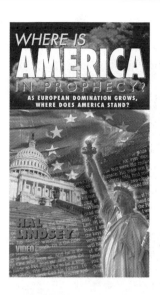

WHERE IS AMERICA IN PROPHECY?

One of the most frequently asked questions by Christians today is, "Where does America fit in prophecy about the last days?" This has been a disturbing question for Hal Lindsey for more than 10 years. Here is the United States, the undisputed leader of the West since World War II, the only true Super Power in the world today, and yet it is not mentioned in the last days prophecies. But another power is clearly predicted to lead the West and then the World in the climactic events that precede the Second Coming of Jesus Christ. According to the prophets, a revived form of the old Roman people and culture, in the form of ten strong nations, will rise to take over the West. Prophets like the Apostle John and Daniel foresaw a precise scenario regarding the alignment of powers in the last days. And the U.S. is not a world leader in these predictions. The inescapable conclusion is that something catastrophic will occur specifically to America. You will not want to miss this compelling analysis of what could soon happen to the United States. Available on VHS and DVD. Please specify format when ordering.

Video ISBN 1-931628-02-5 . . . .$19.99 plus S/H
DVD ISBN 1-931628-09-2 . . . .$19.99 plus S/H

VANISHED — INTO THIN AIR

Visions of the future as portrayed by popular books and films include post-apocalyptic scenes, darkened skies and chaos. Those images are in complete harmony with the prophecies regarding the Last Days contained in the Book of the Revelation. But Revelation also talks of another prophecy, the promise of the Rapture of the Church. Hal Lindsey answers your questions about doctrinal issues surrounding the Rapture of the Church in clear, easy to understand terms in Vanished—Into Thin Air.

ISBN 1-888848-43-X . . . . .Book $12.99 plus S/H

LAST DAYS CHRONICLES

We are living in the last days—the evidence is all around us. The Last Days Chronicles is an exciting new newspaper dedicated to examining that evidence—taken directly from the daily news. Each month, you will see how what looks like chaos to the world, is proof positive that God's Plan for the human race is moving forward according to a clearly defined, pre-determined schedule.

If you would like to receive this exciting new monthly newspaper, please call 1-800-TITUS 35.

Suggested donation for yearly subscription $38.50.

The Stuffed Animals Get Ready for Bed

Alison
Inches

Illustrated by
Bryan Langdo

Harcourt, Inc.

Orlando   Austin   New York   San Diego   Toronto   London

www.HarcourtBooks.com

Library of Congress Cataloging-in-Publication Data
Inches, Alison.
The stuffed animals get ready for bed/Alison Inches;
illustrated by Bryan Langdo.
p. cm.
Summary: Rhyming text describes a young girl's efforts
to put her unruly stuffed animals to bed.
[1. Bedtime—Fiction. 2. Toys—Fiction. 3. Stories in rhyme.]
I. Langdo, Bryan, ill. II. Title.
PZ8.3.I55Stu 2006
[E]—dc22   2005025454
ISBN-13: 978-0-15-216466-9 ISBN-10: 0-15-216466-9

First edition
A C E G H F D B

Manufactured in China

The illustrations in this book were done in watercolor
on Fabriano Artistico cold-press 140-lb. paper.
The display type was set in Family Dog Fat.
The text type was set in Family Dog.
Color separations by Bright Arts Ltd., Hong Kong
Manufactured by South China Printing Company, Ltd., China
This book was printed on totally chlorine-free Stora Enso Matte paper.
Production supervision by Pascha Gerlinger
Designed by April Ward

To our beloved Hunter
and all his stuffed animals
—A. I.

For my parents
—B. L.

My stuffed animals
are wild—
not sleepy at all.

Tumbling and twirling,
they dance down the hall.

They slide and they squeal—
one stands on his head.

How can I get these guys
ready for bed?

My furry panda goes
scrub-a-dub-dub.

Hush, furry panda—
get out of the tub.

My scruffy monkey
bangs a pot on his head.

Hush, scruffy monkey—
hop into your bed.

My polka-dot pig
plays electric guitar.

Hush, dotted pig—
wish on a star.

My little red hen
eats alphabet soup.

Hush, little hen—
climb into your coop.

My fluffy kitten
hides under
the rug.

Hush,
fluffy kitten—
give me a hug.

My spotted cow sings
songs to the lambies.

Hush, spotted cow—
put on your jammies.

My slippery snake
slithers and hisses.

Hush, slippery snake—
blow me some kisses.

My velvety horse
asks for some light.

Hush,
velvety horse—
now say
good night.

My shaggy llama
winds up his clock.

Hush, shaggy llama—
hush-hush and ticktock.

My scaly dragon
stretches and yawns.

Hush, scaly dragon—
the curtains are drawn.

The time has come
to say your good-nights.

Hush, cuddly ones—
turn out the lights.

Now my
stuffed animals
are safe as can be.

Settled and quiet,
they watch over me.